From Conflict To Caring

A Workbook For

Do I Have To Give Up Me To Be Loved By You?
&
If You *Really* Loved Me...

Drs. Jordan Paul & Margaret Paul

Forthcoming from CompCare Publishers.

All inquiries and requests to reprint should be addressed to:

CompCare Publishers
2415 Annapolis Lane
Minneapolis, MN 55441

Cover design by Susan Rinek
Interior design by Mark Heliger

ISBN: 0-912389-01-X

First edition published by:

Evolving Publications
2531 Sawtelle Blvd. #42
Los Angeles, California 90064

ACKNOWLEDGEMENTS

Thanks to all Intention Training Graduates:

> Your willingness to participate in the workshop gave us the opportunity to develop these exercises.

A special thanks to Jackie Benster:

> Your tireless efforts, intense dedication, and creative ideas were an integral part of shaping this book.

TABLE OF CONTENTS

INTRODUCTION TO SECTION I 2

CHAPTER 1 FROM CONFLICT TO CARING **5**
    Loving Behavior 5
    Chart–The Paths Through Conflict 11
    Self-Limiting Beliefs 13
    An Emotional, Intellectual, Philosophical, and Spiritual Journey 14
    The Ego vs. the Higher Self 16
    The Basic Error in Our Thinking 19
    Addictive Relationships in an Addictive Society 23
        Co-dependence: Addictive Relationships 23
        Takers 24
        Caretakers 25
LET THERE BE PEACE ON EARTH 28

CHAPTER 2 Our Personal Odyssey
              –Untangling a Co-dependent System **29**
    Jordan 30
    Margie 38
    Both of Us 48

INTRODUCTION TO SECTION II **53**
FAITH 58

CHAPTER 3 Loving Behavior **59**
    Definition of Loving Behavior 60
    Exercise 1–Self-Limiting Beliefs That Get in the Way
        of Loving Behavior 62
    Exercise 2–Finding Your Higher Self 63
    Exercise 3–Taking Responsibility 69
        3A–The Ways You Believe Yourself to be a Victim 69
        3B–Finding the Loving Behavior. 70
        –Format for Exercise 3B 79
    Exercise 4–Checklist–Self-Limiting Beliefs about Responsibility 80
    Exercise 5–Learning from Unmet Expectations 82
    Exercise 6–Checklist–Self-Limiting Beliefs about Expectations 83
        6A–Checklist–Self-Limiting Beliefs about Expectations
        for Children 85
    Exercise 7–Reviewing the Day for Loving and Unloving Behavior 86

THE ROSE 87

CHAPTER 4 FORMATS FOR LEARNING **89**
    Exercise 8–Basic Format for Learning from a Conflict 92
    The Most Common Self-Limiting Beliefs 93
    Exercise 9–Format for Challenging Self-Limiting Beliefs 94
    Exercise 10–Exploring Beliefs about Issues of Right and Wrong 95
        –Format for Exercise 10 96
    Exercise 11–Learning from Your Feelings 97
        –Format for Exercise 11 98
    Exercise 12–Format for Learning from Your Reaction to
        an Emotional Violation 99
    Exercise 13–Questions to Ask When Wanting to Know Another 100
SYMPTOMS OF INNER PEACE 101

CHAPTER 5 MOVING OUT OF PROTECTIONS **103**
    Exercise 14–The Learning Letter 103
        –Format for Exercise 14 106
    Exercise 15–Passive Listening...108
        Listen 109
    Exercise 16–Active Listening 111
        –Format for Exercise 16 113
    Exercise 17–Breaking a Power Struggle and Learning from It 114
        –Format for Exercise 17 116
        17A–Checklist–Self-Limiting Beliefs about
           Being Right/Wrong...119
    Summary: Ways to Dissolve Protections....................................120
MAKING A DIFFERENCE 121

CHAPTER 6 PROTECTIONS & CONSEQUENCES **123**
    PROTECTIONS..123
    The Controlling Position..125
    Exercise 18–How Do You Look and Sound When
        You're Attempting to Control?.......................................130
        –Format for Exercise 18 131
        18A–Checklist–The Ways You Attempt to Control Others .132
        18B–Check Off Limiting Beliefs about Control. 133
    The Compliant/Rebellious/Indifferent Position................................135
    Exercise 19–Looking at Compliance/Emotional Caretaking............135
        19A–How Do You Rationalize Compliance?......................136
        19B–Checklist–The Compliant Position 137
        19C–Checklist–Self-Limiting Beliefs about Compliance......139
    Exercise 20–Looking at Resistance/Rebellion 140
        20A–Checklist–The Resistant/Rebellious Position 142
        20B–Checklist–Self-Limiting Beliefs about

Resistance/Rebellion..143
Exercise 21–Looking at Resistance/Indifference 144
   21A–Checklist–Self-Limiting Beliefs about Indifference 145
CONSEQUENCES OF PROTECTIONS 146
Exercise 22–The Scenario of Your Protections and Their
   Consequences..150
Exercise 23–The Consequences of Your Protections........151
   23A–Checklist–Negative Consequences of Protections 152
   23B–Checklist–Self-Limiting Beliefs about Protections and
   Consequences..155
DO YOU ACT - OR REACT?..157

CHAPTER 7 ACKNOWLEDGING AND RESPECTING FEAR **159**
Exercise 24–Fears about Relationships with Other People 162
Exercise 25–Exploring Fears of Inadequacy.....................163
   25A–Exploring Beliefs about Fears of Inadequacy 165
   25B–Checklist–Self-Limiting Beliefs about
   Adequacy and Lovability....................................166
   25C–Fears about Learning 168
Exercise 26–Exploring Fear of Pain.................................169
   26A–Exploring Beliefs about Fear of Pain 170
   26B–Checklist–Self-Limiting Beliefs about Pain.................171
Exercise 27–True Communication..................................172
   –Format for Exercise 27 173
Exercise 28–Telling the Truth......................................174
   –Format for Exercise 28 176
LET GO..177

CHAPTER 8 HEALING...**179**
Exercise 29–Compassion, Sadness and Forgiveness.........183
   –Format for Exercise 29 188
   29A–Checklist–Limiting Beliefs about Forgiveness.............193
Exercise 30–Healing Childhood Pain..............................194
   –Format for Exercise 30 195
Exercise 31–Self-Forgiveness and Self-Love 200
THE WAY OF TRANSFORMATION 202

CHAPTER 9 CONTINUING THE PROCESS...........................**203**
Exercise 32–Being a Helper 205
Exercise 33–Observing as A Third Party 207
Exercise 34–Two Couples Helping Each Other 209
Exercise 35–Appreciating Your Life 210
Exercise 36–Join a Support Group.................................213
Exercise 37–The Learning Log 217
Recommended Reading...218

PRINCIPLES FOR RELATIONSHIPS

1. *My relationships are my opportunity to express myself as a loving person. How I express my love is a function of my own willingness to do so, not the result of how another person behaves.*

2. *Any difficult or painful moment in my relationships is a new opportunity for me to develop as a loving person. At the moment of conflict, I can choose to blame the other and the relationship, or, by my willingness to learn from the experience, use the occasion to expand more fully my ability to love and learn.*

3. *I am the one who generates my experience of my relationships through how I choose to act and react to whatever anyone does, and I am solely responsible for my feelings.*

4. *All my life's partners (mate, children, parents, friends, business associates) love me in their Higher Selves as I love them in my Higher Self. My life partners are lovable in their Higher Selves as I am lovable in my Higher Self.*

5. *I can experience love and satisfaction whenever I choose. These feelings are possible at any time and place and in any circumstance, whenever I choose to be who I really am, my Higher Self.*

INTRODUCTION

For the last twenty-three years, we have been in a process of learning and developing ideas about how relationships work, crystallizing these thoughts into models to understanding the paths through conflicts in relationships and finally sharing what we've learned with you.

There are two primary reasons we decided to write this workbook. First is for the many people who have communicated with us asking for more help in implementing the ideas we presented in *Do I Have to Give Up Me to Be Loved By You?* and *If You Really Loved Me...* In response to these requests we created the Intention Training Workshop. This workbook contains some of the information and exercises from the workshop. In the workshop, the learning is facilitated by the group interactions, guided imagery with music, and demonstrations. The workshop is a joyous experience for us to teach and adds different dimensions to the learning experience. We would love to share it with you someday. Until that day, this book offers the tools for you to recreate an on-going, in-depth, learning process.

The second reason for this book is to update our readers regarding our learning over the past six years. Although our basic theory has remained intact, we have deepened our knowledge of it considerably and can therefore communicate with more clarity and impact.

Throughout most of our life together, our most profound learning has come about as a result of our conflicts with each other. What we have learned, we have taken into other relationships–children, parents, friends, ex-mates, clients, siblings, employees–and as a result, have improved these relationships. In the past six years, we have become increasingly aware of the possibilities and tremendous value of learning from each of the relationships in our lives.

Whenever there is conflict with anyone, you can learn from your reactions to that conflict. Our own children have given us

2

wonderful opportunities to practice learning from our reactions. To behave in ways that leave us feeling best about *ourselves* when they behave in ways that frighten us and/or go against the values which we believe to be "right" is quite a challenge. (This, of course goes hand in hand with behaving in ways that are best for them as well.)

Our relationships with our parents and grandparents also give us wonderful opportunities to practice loving behavior. Our patterned ways of behaving with them go back to the roots of our decisions about how to behave. Learning how to be loving with them often means undoing very deeply ingrained habits with attached beliefs that are crucial for us to challenge and resolve.

While the relationships in our immediate family have presented more obvious situations for us to confront ourselves, we also have recognized the importance of learning and changing our ways in other relationships. As our experience and understanding of relationships with others has grown, we realized that in actual fact *our feelings about ourselves are affected by how we relate to everyone.* For example, although it's easy to be a controller with employees, it's only by our commitment to behaving in caring ways that we have the opportunity to confront our fears of letting go and being taken advantage of or being perceived as weak. Since being taken advantage of is certainly not loving to ourselves, we must learn what we need to do to bring our behavior into line with the principles of love. Our relationship with Jackie, our office manager and assistant, has been a wonderful opportunity to practice these principles. The time we've taken to explore and learn when we've had conflicts has really worked well for all of us. We have taken the time to resolve our issues as they arise and before they escalate into growing resentments and dissatisfactions. Jackie won't be with us forever since moving toward her potential will take her beyond the needs of this job, but as long as we're together, we will all use the relationship for our personal development. She has the freedom to confront us with anything that she sees and feels about either of us. We're committed to remaining open to learning and so is she.

Friends are another important part of our lives. Our best friendships are those where we each are willing to be honest with each other. We value those people who are willing to confront us when they feel unloved by our behavior. That is the way we can continue to grow, learn, and become even better friends. People, especially those who have risen to powerful positions, often surround themselves with others who are intimidated by them. They often will get rid of anyone who begins to come into his/her own personal power. This effectively cuts off one of the best sources of feedback necessary for continuing personal growth.

As therapists, we have often learned from being open to our clients' reactions to us. For example, if clients are defensive or resistant, it is very easy to make them wrong for their reactions and focus on helping them change, rather than seeing our part in their reaction.

The book is divided into two sections. Section I contains two chapters to bring you, the reader, up to date with our ideas. Other new information will be sprinkled throughout the book as we introduce each exercise. Section II (which will have its own introduction) contains the practical exercises you can use to increase your personal awareness and create changes in your life.

In between the chapters you will find a divider page with a poem, song, excerpt, saying, etc. We have found these to be meaningful inspiration and fun to have around and hope you enjoy them as well. We have tried, whenever possible, to solve the pronoun problem by using "him" in one chapter and "her" in the next.

A more complete expression of our ideas are in *Do I Have to Give Up Me To Be Loved By You?* and *If You Really Loved Me...* It would be valuable, but not necessary, for you to be familiar with these books.

Jordan and Margaret Paul
West Los Angeles
March, 1988

CHAPTER

·1·

FROM CONFLICT TO CARING

LOVING BEHAVIOR

In *Do I Have to Give Up Me to Be Loved By You?*, when we first developed our model of the paths through conflict, we understood that the closed, defensive and protected path necessarily leads to negative consequences. Also, we knew that the open, vulnerable and learning path leads to positive consequences. And we knew that all of us can choose which path to take.

For example, let's say that your mate forgets your birthday and you feel upset. You can protect yourself by blaming your partner...who may then get angry...which hurts you...and then you both make a retreat, sulking at different ends of the house, alone and miserable, each feeling unloved and unloving. Or you can gently remind him or her, openly ask the reasons for the forgetting, explore your reactions (why you've taken it personally, your expectations and how you react when your expectations aren't met) and experience the entirely different result that follows acting from an intent to learn. Clearly, however, the choice of the reaction is yours. *Also, you can see that, as you make your choice, the things you do generate the feelings you feel.*

The most important addition to this understanding of the paths through conflict emerged when we discovered, in *The Road Less Traveled* by M. Scott Peck, the following definition: "{Loving behavior is} the will to extend one's self for the purpose of nurturing one's own or another's spiritual growth." This sparked thoughts which added a much deeper dimension to our thinking–the dimension of love and the caring and the recognition of the difference between loving feelings and loving behavior. (We will use loving and caring interchangeably.)

First, for most people there is a big difference between the love they say they feel and their behavior. In general, saying one thing and doing another was not a new idea, but to look at love this way was. When conflict presents itself, people who say they love each other all too often do not act out the love they feel. Instead, they act out their protections.

Second, conversely to the statement in italics above, the feelings you feel generate the things you do. So, if on a deep level you love someone, but your behavior isn't loving, there must be another feeling that is getting in the way. Almost every time, that intervening feeling is some form of fear. As we said in *Do I Have to Give Up Me to Be Loved By You?*, the opposite of love is not hate, it is fear.

The next conclusion became obvious: the intent to learn, which we had labeled the path of evolution, is the path of growth all right, but more important, it is the path of loving behavior. And the opposite, the path of fear and protection, is unloving behavior.

We have therefore expanded our definition as follows: *Loving behavior nurtures your own and another's emotional and spiritual growth, promotes personal responsibility and increases your self-esteem.*

Our model illustrates the only two intentions possible in a conflict—the intent to learn or the intent to protect—and the paths that inexorably follow each intent. Conflict is any situation which produces upsetting feelings—fear, guilt, anger, disappointment, hurt. It occurs when another person does something you don't like or think is wrong, or when you do something and another person becomes upset or you fear the other person may become upset with you. The instantaneous, learned reaction to conflict is to protect. You choose it, albeit subconsciously, because the conflict taps into many fears and you believe that reacting openly would leave you too vulnerable. These deeply ingrained beliefs and fears, learned in childhood, lie buried in your subconscious and you are probably unaware of them. You have been reacting to conflicts protectively since you were an infant and the responses have become habit. In addition, you may never have witnessed anything other than a protective reaction to conflict. Your fears and beliefs produce the patterned responses that run your life.

There are three categories of protective reactions: 1) Control–attempting to get others to change their behavior by creating fear or guilt in them; 2) Compliance–going along with what others want out of fear or guilt; 3) Non-compliance–either active resistance, which is rebelling; passive resistance which is temporary compliance followed by deferred resistance (you say you will but then you don't); or indifference, which is either withdrawing or shutting out, or both. *None of the things you do to protect yourself*–those behaviors that cover up your vulnerable feelings of hurt and fear–*meet the definition of loving behavior.*

We (Margie & Jordan) were aware of our protective behaviors. It is relatively simple to see that attempts to control people (getting angry, criticism, etc.) or giving ourselves up were not leading to intimacy. But to realize that these behaviors were unloving hit us like a ton of bricks.

It is easy to be loving when things go your way, but when people do things you don't like, it taps into that deep well of subconscious fear from which springs your protective, defensive, unloving behavior. You lovingly care for your newborn until he/she does something that upsets you. You fall in love and nurture and support each other–until you get upset and believe it's the other person's fault.

You also react habitually with protective, unloving behavior when you do something that results in another person getting upset and behaving in an unloving way towards you. You give in, hoping to placate others and eventually gain their love, resist their attempts to change you by becoming rebellious or walling off behind your indifference, or attempt to get others to change their unloving behavior. They then react to your defenses with their own defenses and a protective circle is created.

Understanding loving behavior made it disturbingly evident that unhappiness is always a direct result of unloving behavior.

To see compliant behavior as unloving is a real stretch for most people. After all, you have been taught that giving in, going along with, and/or pleasing others at your own expense is loving. But seeing that none of these behaviors fosters your own or others' emotional and spiritual growth casts an entirely different light on your behavior.

Unloving behavior starts the erosion process that leads to alienation and unhappiness, instead of optimism, joy and peace. The unspoken message you give over and over again to the people in your life is, "I'll be caring with you as long as you behave the way I think you should."

Not only do protective, unloving behaviors estrange you from the people in your life, they also cause unhappiness within you. Protective behavior does not nurture your own emotional and spiritual growth and is not personally responsible. Consequently, protective, unloving behavior diminishes your self-esteem.

The corollary insight is just as important and may be more surprising: your own self-esteem is raised or lowered by how you react to upsetting situations. Protective responses–attempting to control, giving in, becoming indifferent–lower self-esteem. You feel weak, out of control, like a victim. Loving behavior, an openness to learning, feels powerful. You are in control of yourself; you are not a reactor but are taking positive action. (This is the focus of our next book, *Becoming Your Own Hero/ine.*)

Protections–your attempts to avoid the pain of losing either another person's love or your own integrity–actually bring about the very things you hope to avoid. Protections always lead to negative consequences, such as lowered self-esteem; eroding love; power struggles; sexual, financial, communication squabbles; feeling unloved and unloving.

Protective, unloving circles continue to bring about the misery in your life. Anytime you see the other person's behavior as wrong and try to get him/her to stop, or go along with it out of guilt or fear, or become indifferent, you perpetuate an unloving circle.

The intent to learn, on the other hand, fits the definition of loving behavior and produces entirely different results. It is personally responsible behavior, nurtures emotional and spiritual growth and leads to the joy, intimacy, satisfaction, emotional growth and the self-esteem that you want. Anything other than an intent to learn is protective.

When you want to learn, you're open to learning everything you can about what the conflict has to teach you. You want to learn about yourself and the other person. You want to learn from your feelings rather than protect against them. The intent to learn begins a process of exploration which requires *only two* conditions: 1) a willingness to experience the transitory pain which may accompany the truth; and 2) a belief that there are very important, compelling, respectable reasons behind every behavior and feeling. The areas that can be explored and learned about are: how you protect; what happens when you protect; the fears and beliefs that produce your protections; how you got these fears and beliefs and the purpose it now serves to continue to believe them; what it means to take personal responsibility and to be loving; and what are the fears and beliefs that are getting in the way of behaving in that way.

When we wrote *Do I Have to Give Up Me to Be Loved By You*, our primary focus was on exploring and learning about the other person. We have learned, however, that the primary focus must be on learning about oneself. Learning about the other is important and valuable but focusing on oneself is the key to being personally responsible. In fact, focusing on the other can be just another way to protect oneself from looking inward and taking responsibility.

One of the questions we are most commonly asked is, "How can I practice these ideas if the person I'm in conflict with is not open to exploring and learning?" When your intent is to learn about yourself, another person is merely your helper. You can do your learning with or without him/her. In a primary love relationship, the involvement of your mate creates a wonderful intimacy which is not possible if you do your own learning or do your learning with another person. But if you believe you can't learn without the involvement of the person you are in conflict with, you become a victim, anxiously awaiting the other person's decision to be open or not. However, the belief that you must wait for another's cooperation is not true. You only become a victim by choice. When the other person is not available you can learn about yourself by

9

looking at your part in creating the difficulties you are having. You can read, think, or write by yourself or enlist the help of a friend or therapist.

We all want love, and wait for others to give it to us, but love and good feelings occur in our lives only as we become more loving. The charge becomes obvious: You need to let go of trying to get others to change and concentrate on what *you* need to do to become more loving.

Our up-to-date revised chart follows, illustrating the paths through conflict.

THE PATHS THROUGH CONFLICT

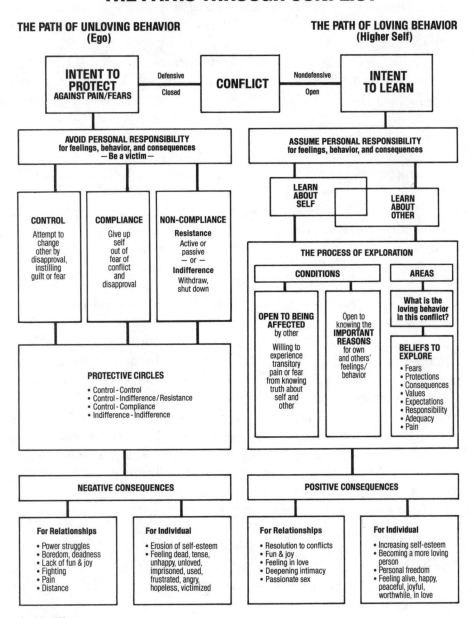

THE PATH OF UNLOVING BEHAVIOR
(Ego)

THE PATH OF LOVING BEHAVIOR
(Higher Self)

| INTENT TO PROTECT AGAINST PAIN/FEARS | Defensive / Closed | CONFLICT | Nondefensive / Open | INTENT TO LEARN |

AVOID PERSONAL RESPONSIBILITY
for feelings, behavior, and consequences
— Be a victim —

ASSUME PERSONAL RESPONSIBILITY
for feelings, behavior, and consequences

LEARN ABOUT SELF

LEARN ABOUT OTHER

CONTROL
Attempt to change other by disapproval, instilling guilt or fear

COMPLIANCE
Give up self out of fear of conflict and disapproval

NON-COMPLIANCE
Resistance
Active or passive
— or —
Indifference
Withdraw, shut down

THE PROCESS OF EXPLORATION

CONDITIONS

AREAS

What is the loving behavior in this conflict?

OPEN TO BEING AFFECTED
by other

Willing to experience transitory pain or fear from knowing truth about self and other

Open to knowing the **IMPORTANT REASONS** for own and others' feelings/ behavior

BELIEFS TO EXPLORE
• Fears
• Protections
• Consequences
• Values
• Expectations
• Responsibility
• Adequacy
• Pain

PROTECTIVE CIRCLES
• Control - Control
• Control - Indifference / Resistance
• Control - Compliance
• Indifference - Indifference

NEGATIVE CONSEQUENCES

POSITIVE CONSEQUENCES

For Relationships
• Power struggles
• Boredom, deadness
• Lack of fun & joy
• Fighting
• Pain
• Distance

For Individual
• Erosion of self-esteem
• Feeling dead, tense, unhappy, unloved, imprisoned, used, frustrated, angry, hopeless, victimized

For Relationships
• Resolution to conflicts
• Fun & joy
• Feeling in love
• Deepening intimacy
• Passionate sex

For Individual
• Increasing self-esteem
• Becoming a more loving person
• Personal freedom
• Feeling alive, happy, peaceful, joyful, worthwhile, in love

11

The intent to learn in conflict is rare. Yet it is the only way you can learn the lessons that will lead you out of your unhappiness and into love. Any situation which is upsetting gives you the opportunity for your most profound learning. Unmet expectations, disappointments, broken commitments, others behaving in uncaring ways toward you or toward themselves, another person not wanting to talk with you, differences in wants or needs, being treated in what you believe to be an unfair manner–all of these could be met with either the intent to protect or the intent to learn. When you react protectively, you do not learn anything. An openness to learn is how you create meaningful changes in your life.

In every conflict situation, the question never asked is, "What is the loving behavior?" Because you haven't been trained to think in these terms, you need to learn what is loving and then you can learn what gets in the way of behaving that way. An openness to learning is always loving. Reacting in your protective, unloving ways will guarantee you always wind up feeling bad. It's the same state of consciousness that guarantees war between nations. We get upset, believe we're right ("God is on *our* side!"), and go to war. Or we defend ourselves from a real or imagined threat by going to war. Even though at times fighting may be necessary to survive a real situation that threatens our survival (such as in World War II), we have never used the time between wars to learn the lessons that would lead to the shift in thinking necessary to bring about peace on earth. For example, the belief that you can bring about peace by going to war is a false belief. *Real peace will only emerge from a total change in consciousness.* Learning what it means to relate to others with love is that consciousness. This means everyone in your life, especially your spouse, children, and parents.

Reading the written history of our culture illustrates a distressing picture of an unloving people. Love has been preached but not practiced. Ego consciousness–judgmentalness, self-righteousness, dominance, one-upmanship, selfishness, accumulation of power–has been predominant. The only thing that has changed in the way people have reacted to conflict is the weapons used. Now we are at a unique crossroads, either we learn to live in peace or we will destroy our planet. As groups that have been denied equality (women, blacks, children) claim their rights to equal status, all institutions must change or crumble. Only when we become convinced that our old ways of thinking will never work to bring about peace and joy will we be ready to behave from a totally different consciousness–the consciousness of love. And the beginning is learning to relate lovingly to each other in our everyday lives.

Relationship then, is the new frontier and we are the pioneers. It's both frightening and exciting. There are not any models to help us learn how to play this new game. Most books that teach relationships have reflected old ways of thinking. Everyone is struggling to discover what it means to have truly loving relationships with each other. We're all in this together. No one has all the answers. But as we help each other piece together the fabric of a new quilt, we can unlock the potential of human beings to live more closely with the part of ourselves that has been long dormant–our Higher Selves, the consciousness of love that lies within us all. As we live more in harmony with that consciousness, we will open new possibilities for human beings to become...well, who knows what?

SELF-LIMITING BELIEFS

Removing the blocks to being a more loving person has become the focus of our teaching. Reacting protectively is always in reaction to fear and becoming tight, judgmental, self-righteous, defensive, and self-centered is exactly opposite to loving, which is to be open, giving (without giving up oneself), soft, and concerned for self and others. *The real basis of fear is false beliefs*. In fact, all negative feelings come from beliefs. So although you can't change your feelings directly, you can change your beliefs and then your feelings will change. Beliefs run your life and most of your beliefs are erroneous and self-limiting.

For example, when you believe you're not adequate in a

particular area (how your body looks, your intelligence, your sensitivity), you take things personally, feeling bad and defensive when you're criticized. Your feelings come directly from that belief. When you know you're okay, even though others' criticism never feels good, you don't react with the bad feelings that come from feeling wrong. You clearly see that the criticism comes from the other person's false beliefs and his or her own unhealed pain, and your feelings and reactions are entirely different.

You may not fully understand how your beliefs create the fears that generate your behavior. In fact, you may not believe it at all. However, we'll be coming back to it over and over again. In fact, throughout this book you will find lists of self-limiting beliefs. You will probably be astounded to discover how many self-limiting beliefs you have.

You'll find enough self-limiting beliefs in this workbook to keep you working on yourself for the rest of your life, and we have only included a small portion of them. The intention to learn from conflicts provides the explorations which seek to rid yourself of false beliefs and live more consistently with the truth, the universal truths.

AN EMOTIONAL, INTELLECTUAL, PHILOSOPHICAL, AND SPIRITUAL JOURNEY

You were not born with beliefs about right or wrong. From conception through birth and after birth, you were guided by an unseen intelligence that knew exactly how to behave and feel. You didn't think, you just reacted. The beliefs you later used to guide your life were learned. The truth you now seek in the learning process comes from the part of yourself that we refer to as the Higher Self. The Higher Self has been called by many names—the Holy Spirit, Christ Consciousness, natural self, human nature, God. You can use whatever feels most comfortable for you.

This Higher Self is an extension of the energy that created and maintains everything. It is the part of you that knows how to live in a loving and joyful way. The intention to learn is a journey to rediscover and live more harmoniously with that part of yourself.

The Higher Self state of being is usually not well known. The personality you formed soon after birth is the more familiar. This learned persona is your ego.

We're defining the ego as it is used in Eastern philosophy–the constructed personality, the false self. The definition of ego in Western thinking has come from Freudian or psychoanalytic psychology. By that definition, the ego is part of the personality structure which includes the ego, superego, and the id. The ego is the governor and therefore a strong ego is a healthy thing. But when defined as the false self, having a dominant ego is not desirable.

As you grew up, your constructed personality or ego was an important part of your development and became your defense system. You came into the world defenseless, guided mostly by instinct, your natural self. Your behavior, however, was judged by just about everyone. Judgments may have been anything from a disapproving look to yelling, spanking or isolation. But the message was clear, "You are wrong." You were made wrong for your thoughts, feelings and actions. You were made wrong every time your behavior conflicted with what those around you believed was the right way to be. You were made wrong by the attempts of others to teach you the "right" way to be. Into the ego went all of the beliefs you learned.

The ego was created, then, to protect you from the disapproval suffered when your natural actions and feelings brought disapproval from those around you. As a child, the fear of rejection was so great that you had to create a way to avoid disapproval and gain the love you so desperately needed. Your ego was necessary; it saved your sanity, if not your life.

The ego, born out of fear, does not know how to love. It is the needy part of you that only wants to get, to manipulate others to give you love, affirmation, approval. All fears of inadequacy and the beliefs that created these fears are in your ego.

For most of us our personality becomes so identified with our ego that we totally forget we have another part of our being. That other part is your Higher Self. It is the part of you that is connected to, and in harmony with, the universe. It functions from universal truths rather than the beliefs of human beings. It is the best that is within you. In the Higher Self there are no judgments, fears, worries or protections. The Higher Self is the place of unconditional love and knowingness. The Higher Self is love. It is important to recognize that the Higher Self exists in all of us and we all have access to that part of us.

It's important to recognize times when you've been in harmony with that part of you and recognize the feelings that always accompany Higher Self behavior. (We have included an exercise to help you do that on Page 63.) It is that centered, balanced wholesome place, where you act with integrity, where you feel your self-esteem enhanced instead of eroded. When your behavior comes from the Higher Self, you feel like you're walking on water as opposed to being stuck in the quagmire of your ego's emotions.

THE EGO VS. THE HIGHER SELF

All negative feelings come from the ego. The Higher Self knows only peace, love and joy. The ego tries to justifies unloving behavior–"He deserved it," "I had to teach him a lesson," "It was for her own good." The Higher Self would never act in an unloving way no matter what another person is doing. In essence, that is the message as taught by Buddha, Jesus, Mohammed, Gandhi, Martin Luther King, Mother Theresa, Rabbi Hillel.

The Higher Self is the spiritual part of you and the only true reality. The ego is fear. The Higher Self is love. You cannot be in fear and in love at the same time, you can only be in one or the other. So in your Higher Self, free from fear, you flow and feel alive, joyful, relaxed.

The false beliefs of the ego will tell you that you are too vulnerable and need to be protected, forcing you to act in unloving defensive ways. Your protections create deadness, depression, anger and tension. The Higher Self knows the false threat in things and knows the truth–*you can handle, survive, and find peace in any situation.* Do you believe that?

Your ego is probably having a field day, pointing out all kinds of situations that you can't handle: your mate leaves you, has an affair, won't make love with you, dies; your boss gets angry with you; you get fired from your job; your business fails; your child fails in school, gets hung up on drugs. Philosophically, any situation can be learned from and turned into a positive experience. Haven't you known people who have faced these situations and worse and turned them into opportunities? Only when *you* know that any conflict is an opportunity can you accept turmoil, chaos, and unhappiness into your life rather than protecting against them.

All of the beliefs that the ego has are lies. One of the most commonly held false beliefs is that happiness and self-esteem come from outside of yourself. Therefore, most people pursue happiness and self-esteem by trying to become successful (accomplishing things, accumulating wealth, status, a good reputation), and/or being loved. But behind the closed doors of protected thinking, you are unable to discover the truth: even if you become all the things that are supposed to make you feel better about yourself, there is a necessary element that if not part of your life will negate everything else you do.

That element is how you react to difficult, upsetting situations in your life. You have been led to believe that you will feel good about yourself when you get love, so most of your behavior is an attempt to get approval (or avoid disapproval) and is, therefore, manipulative or defensive. And yet, it's *only when you give love that your self-esteem, your self-worth is raised.* "Giving love" means "that behavior which nurtures emotional and spiritual growth."

The thing that the ego doesn't tell you is that the only way you come to find real happiness within yourself, peace within yourself, love in your life and self-esteem is when you behave in loving ways. Things like money and a relationship can *enhance* your joy, but will never *create* joy.

Protected, you get angry when things don't go your way, on

your time table, by your form. Open, you recognize that there is a higher wisdom guiding your life and you can tap into that knowing for guidance through seemingly your darkest hours. You can wallow in the misery of self-righteous indignation, or learn your lessons. You can stay stuck or you can get on with your life moving into higher self-esteem and joy. You always have two choices–to protect or to learn.

The intent to learn is a choice that you can make at any time. We all would like to believe that our emotions dictate our lives so that we really don't have choice. We always have choice. At the Intention Training Foundation, we have a symbol that's formed by your index and middle fingers held up in a V in front of your face. The left finger represents the intention to protect, the right finger the intention to learn. The choice is always right in front of you.

You may be feeling very angry, critical and disapproving of yourself right now. Those thoughts are coming from your ego. When you're hard on yourself, remember that you are like a television set with only two channels. When you're critical, you're turned to your fear channel and you're hearing the voice of your ego. But playing on the other channel, your love channel, is your Higher Self. Your Higher Self, being nonjudgmental, is never critical and knows that all things have a purpose, a time, a reason. You can tune in anytime you want and listen to the voice of your Higher Self. (This is a powerful therapeutic tool and this concept will be more fully developed in our forthcoming book on spirituality, *Do I Have to Give Up Me to Be Loved By God?*)

A realistic goal is to have the ego be less in control of your life. The more fear dominates your life, the more unhappy you are. And the more you react in concert and in harmony with your Higher Self, the happier you are with yourself and the more love, intimacy and joy you create around you.

Learning about your ego–its fears and beliefs–is the way out. The more you resolve your fears by bringing your beliefs into alignment with the universal truths, the less time you'll spend in your ego. The task is a challenging and on-going one. You won't resolve them this week, and maybe not even in this lifetime.

THE BASIC ERROR IN OUR THINKING

The most basic error in your thinking is that you are wrong, inadequate, unimportant, unlovable, unworthy, not good enough. Your protections surround this cavern of self-doubt and most of your unhappiness results from your attempts to protect yourself from feeling wrong.

In the course of your life, especially at the beginning, you receive thousands of messages that you're wrong. In *The Magic of Conflict*, Tom Crum quotes a study done in Iowa by graduate students following a normal two-year-old throughout a day. "They observed that the child was told what not to do 432 times, as opposed to 32 positive acknowledgements. The national average of parent-to-child criticisms is 12 to 1–that is, 12 criticisms to 1 compliment. Within the average secondary school classroom, the ratio of criticism to compliments is 18 to 1 between teacher and student." Every time a person gets upset, and doesn't take responsibility for that upset, the person is blaming the child and making the child wrong.

Children have no way of knowing that in the house next door, or in another country, or in another time in history their behavior would not be judged wrong, so while we are still very young, we conclude there is something wrong with us. This most basic error in our thinking totally runs our lives. It results in repressing our natural way of being and becoming approval seekers, trying to find the "right" way to be.

The truth is that parents get upset because the behavior of their children taps into some of the parents' fears. Parents' fears come from their own beliefs. For example, when parents fear that children will grow up to be weak if they are held when they cry, then parents will either ignore their crying children or criticize them ("That's nothing to get upset about!") in an attempt to get their children to be strong. Children take criticism or being ignored personally and feel wrong. Children can't know that they are okay and that any unloving behavior comes from their parents' difficulty in loving. The child winds up feeling unlovable. After years of the

19

message that you're wrong when another person becomes upset with your behavior, is it any wonder why you have such a deep well of self-doubt? Everyone in the world suffers in varying degrees from the insecurity that comes from not feeling okay.

All your emotional fear stems from the belief that you're not adequate or lovable. Your defense system is built on this fear. The fear of being wrong and the defensiveness which follows this fear permeate everything. You hold back, you become closed to learning, and your ability to love is severely crippled.

Although at one time you needed a strong defense system (a predominant ego), as an adult you no longer need this for survival. Unfortunately, it has by now become habitual and very powerful.

You've moved past the fears in some areas but have probably avoided developing the areas where your biggest fears lie. So a person with few fears of his athletic ability might develop that area but avoid his intellectual development and perpetuate the belief of his intellectual inadequacy. Women, who generally speaking have fewer fears than men in the areas of expressing their feelings, will become more comfortable with feelings than the men who repress theirs behind walls of fear. More women, on the other hand, seem to end up with feelings of fear and inadequacy about taking care of themselves financially.

Fear keeps you from the love and self-esteem you so desperately need. All of your attempts to get love or avoid disapproval will never get you the love you need. In fact, everytime you behave in an unloving way it reinforces your belief that you're not lovable.

The basic error in your thinking has led you to the belief that if you can get enough love, you will feel better about yourself. However, as we've stated, your feelings of self-worth cannot come from getting love but will only come from giving love. When you feel so inadequate and unlovable, moving into being loving is a real challenge. The more secure you feel, the more loving you can be. The more you are in your ego the more your self-esteem is eroded. Your immediate reactions are almost always from your ego.

From your well of self-doubt spring your defensive

protections. Taking things personally, you quickly lash back or withdraw. You retreat behind your protections rather than open to learning both about yourself and the other person. When criticized, put down, made wrong, etc., it's very difficult to remain open, curious, soft, and loving. Were you to know the truth–that you are, in fact, not bad or wrong–then when another person gets upset with your behavior, you wouldn't get thrown off your center.

Your center is love. Covering your center are your protective behaviors. Everyone is love under his/her protections. But as soon as we get frightened, up come our protections. The more frightened the individual, the more protected he is. The Hitlers of the world are the most frightened of all. We need to protect ourselves from them without losing sight of the fact that even they are lovable at their core. Admittedly that's a tall order, but it's something to shoot for. Meanwhile, you can start by loving those around you who are behaving in less disastrous, but nonetheless, unloving ways. And, most importantly, you can learn to love yourself when you run into your own non-loving, judgmental ego.

How do you feel about the core of you? When do you judge yourself "wrong"? These are the kinds of questions that will take you on a lifetime journey of learning by questioning the beliefs that limit your self-esteem, joy, and intimacy. Think about the things you were made wrong for. Were you wrong when you expressed sexual curiosity, a desire to play with dolls, an aggressiveness, a dreaminess, rebelliousness, sensitivity, curiosity? Were you made wrong because of how you looked, walked, spoke, thought?

We all behave in unloving ways, at times–unloving to ourselves as well as to others. But your life can become so much better as you become less judgmental. What is the purpose of being judgmental? What is your fear of giving up being judgmental? It is the answer to this last question that will take you to the doorstep of some of your most basic self-limiting beliefs.

Into your ego has gone all of the beliefs you either have been given by others or concluded on your own. The ego contains hundreds of false, self-limiting beliefs. Some of the most prevalent, and the ones that lead to almost all of your unhappiness are:

* You are bad, inadequate, unlovable, unworthy.

* Others are responsible for your feelings or actions. You are a victim, a helpless reactor, powerless over how you feel.

* You are responsible for others' feelings or actions.

* You will find happiness and or inner peace outside of yourself from things like: money, sex, love, drugs, alcohol, approval, clothes, power over others.

* Anger will get you what you want.

* Getting others to give you what you want will make you happy.

* You can't handle pain because you don't know how to find your way through the pain to joy.

When you believe you're wrong or inadequate, then you have to protect yourself. To do this, you: 1) control others to keep their love; 2) give yourself up to keep their love; or 3) shut down to keep from having to deal with the fear of loss. The basic fear that runs our lives is the fear of loss—loss of another's love and/or loss of our self (integrity, identity). Tied to this is the belief that we can't make ourselves happy and so we must depend on others for our happiness. The corollary belief that we're responsible for others' feelings makes addicts out of all of us. As long as we operate from these beliefs we are hopelessly dependent on the people in our lives. Once we're stuck with these beliefs, stuck being protected and unable to move into our Higher Selves and learning, then we become like addicts, helplessly out of control in that area of our lives.

ADDICTIVE RELATIONSHIPS IN AN ADDICTIVE SOCIETY

We have been well trained to become addicts. As children, very few of us are taught how to rely on ourselves for our happiness. Instead, we have been raised to be dependent on things outside of ourselves for our good feelings. Everything from advertisements to love songs have taught us that someone or something will solve our problems for us–whether it's loneliness, alienation, unpopularity, or unhappiness. Or we discovered on our own that we can blot out the reality of our feelings by overeating, becoming stoned in front of the TV, having sex, popping a pill or working excessively.

At the root of all addictions are the many false, self-limiting beliefs we have about ourselves. These are the beliefs about your unlovability, inadequacy, inability to know what's right for you. The years of being told that what you want and feel is wrong has left you lost, seeking answers from outside yourself, running from one pursuit to another searching in all the wrong areas for the answers on how to find happiness, satisfaction, peace, joy, intimacy, intensity, passion, and a love of life.

Co-dependence: Addictive Relationships

Almost everybody believes that happiness comes from connecting to another person, and connection is truly a wonderful experience. However, when you *need* that person to make you feel whole, worthwhile and happy, you are not being personally responsible and not in your Higher Self. What happens with most people is that they don't know how to find themselves on the inside, so their unhappiness is not coming from the lack of connection with the other person, but from a lack of connection with themselves.

Everything you've been taught says that love equals need and the more you need, the greater your love. Every love song you've ever heard tells you things like: "Can't live, if living is without you. Can't give, can't give anymore;" "There's just no me without you." That's pretty drastic. The messages are: "My whole life is dependent on this relationship and without it, I'm nothing." or "I was miserable until you came along and now I'm great" or "I was happy until you left me and now I'm miserable and I'll stay that way the rest of my life."

The promise is that another person giving you love will solve your problems, make you happy, give you the security you desire, make you feel good about yourself, give you the aliveness and clarity that you need to conquer the world. Love does have that power, but when you are dependent on another for happiness, you aren't being personally responsible, and that's not really love. The problem is that you have been led to believe the fairy tale that when you find someone to love you, *then*, only then, will you live happily ever after. A relationship based on this myth will experience a diminishing love as both partners operate from one of two problematic, false beliefs. One is the belief that *we don't have the right to make ourselves happy* because we are flawed in some way. The other is that *we don't have the power within us to take care of our own needs.* When we don't know this, we need to have control over others in order to get it. We become dependent on others for our good feelings (or to dull our painful feelings–loneliness, boredom, unlovableness) and a co-dependent relationship is formed between takers and caretakers.

Takers

Those people whose primary fear comes from the belief that they don't have the power to make themselves happy become predominantly takers. They believe that it's the other person's behavior that is making them unhappy and if only the other would change, then things would be fine. Since they don't believe they are capable of creating their own happiness, they must *get* something from others to be happy. Their manipulation is obvious as they attempt to control others by intimidating them with fear and guilt.

Caretakers

Those people whose primary fear comes from the belief that they don't have the right to make themselves happy become predominantly caretakers. They are compliers, believing it's their responsibility to make others happy. When others are upset, they try to make things right by giving themselves up, hoping that by making others happy, they will be loved and it will be their turn to be happy. "I don't have the right to make myself happy until others are happy" and/or "I don't have the right to make myself happy if others are upset and unhappy with what I am doing." People become caretakers when they believe others don't have the power to do for themselves. They believe others are fragile and see themselves as stronger.

There are caretakers who don't know how to make themselves happy (and are often takers) and those who do, but must wait to make themselves happy until those around them are happy. (They are primarily martyrs.) This kind of controlling is very subtle, but is nevertheless manipulative and, therefore, unloving.

We all, at times, behave as caretakers and takers. However, many people become entrenched in one or the other of these roles, and unloving relationships are the result. Both categories of behavior are motivated by fear. Both roles are needy and focus on getting the other's approval. Neither is loving.

To understand what love is and to become a truly loving person, you must be willing to deal with your dependence on other people. The beliefs that create the protections of being a taker or caretaker go very deep. Changing your role requires a major commitment to the process of freeing yourself from your self-limiting fears and beliefs. Takers must learn how to make themselves happy. Caretakers must be willing to risk losing another's love temporarily or perhaps losing the relationship entirely.

One of the most common fears in co-dependent relationships is being "wrong." To break the hold of this fear, you will have to take inventory of all your beliefs. (This is the central focus in the workbook section of this book.) You must take the time to know what truly makes you happy and what you need to do to bring that about. You must develop faith. And that faith can only develop as you turn your life over more and more to the only thing greater than your ego mind–your Higher Self. The more you have faith in your own Higher Self, the more you become personally powerful and the more you can give up needing the dependent connection. Then you can connect with others in truly loving relationships.

Love is unconditional. Dependent, needy feelings always have strings attached. "I will love you if..." or "If you really loved me, you would..." are the unspoken control mechanisms of conditional love. We give in order to get something: love, connection, approval, safety, affirmation, sex, caring, more communication, a response, change, appreciation. The problem is not in wanting any of these things, it's the attempt to manipulate others to give us what we think we need that creates our difficulties. All of our thinking is tied up in the unloving consciousness of the ego–to get love. Love is a rare commodity.

One of the problems in our thinking about love is believing that "love" means being a caretaker, being nice, giving when somebody doesn't want it, giving when somebody is angry. Loving means loving yourSelf. What is loving to your Higher Self is automatically loving to others. This means taking responsibility for making yourSelf happy.

The way out of all this is to tune into what really makes you feel really good about yourself. It never increases your self-esteem to give in order to get. It doesn't work inside, because if the person doesn't react as you'd hoped, you're miserable. It does make you happy inside when you give because it feels good to you.

People often say, "I've given, and given, and given and I have no more left to give." This usually indicates that they've given themselves up or they've given with strings attached, in order to get love, approval, connection, etc. They continue to give because they feel empty and are trying to get others to fill them up. That is not loving. When you give without expectation of getting something, it always makes you feel wonderful. And that's love.

To be more loving, you must look at the barrier keeping you from behaving that way. What gets in the way is always fear. You can only be in fear or in love. Those are the only two emotional states possible. As soon as you find out what the fear is and what the belief is that's causing the fear, then you can look at the belief and find out where you got it, why you keep it, test it out and, if it's erroneous, you will then be rid of it.

Connecting with your Higher Self puts you on a spiritual path–the path to discover the truth. The spiritual path is the only way out of the problems that have been created by your ego. Since joy, happiness, inner peace, love and intimacy only exist when you are in your Higher Self, the more time you're there, the better your life. Once you accept that there is a source of knowledge other than your ego, you can let go and let your Higher Self take over and guide you. You all have that inner knowing, that infallible guide that will tell you when you're off center, but it needs to be cultivated in order to emerge from the recesses into which it has been stuffed.

It's very frightening to open to a new way of thinking. We are very invested in our traditional ways. Retraining your inner voice from "How do I get love?" to "How do I give love?" will require an effort, but that is where your task lies. Many people will not entertain the notion a Higher Self until their lives are in shambles. However, you don't have to reach crisis–a heart attack, ulcers, cancer, divorce, separation, family disarray, business failure–to realize that you will never get what you want with your fears in control. Hopefully we don't have to destroy our planet before we wake up to the truth of what happens when fear dominates love. It's only through the love of our Higher Selves that we can bring about peace within ourselves, peace within our families, and peace on our planet.

LET THERE BE PEACE ON EARTH

Let there be peace on earth and let it begin with me;

Let there be peace on earth, the peace that was meant to be.

With God as our Father, Brothers all are we.

Let us walk with each other in perfect harmony.

Let peace begin with me, let this be the moment now.

With every step I take, let this be my solemn vow:

To take each moment and live each moment
in peace eternally.

Let there be peace on earth and let it begin with me.

—Jill Jackson and Sy Miller

CHAPTER

·2·

OUR PERSONAL ODYSSEY

UNTANGLING A CO-DEPENDENT SYSTEM

Our spiritual pursuit and beliefs have become increasingly important to us. As with most people, it required a crisis to understand the importance of this aspect of our lives. Although Margie has been drawn to the spiritual for many years, it has become important to Jordan only in the past few years.

With all our knowledge and commitment, our marriage ran into its second critical period about four years ago. The first very difficult period occurred after eight years of marriage and we documented it in *Free To Love*. We learned a great deal from that period and it led to the creation of our Intention Training model. However, we hadn't recognized the underlying difficulties that continued to eat away at our intimacy and in-love feelings. We had uncovered some of the aspects of our control-compliance system and thought we had resolved it but we hadn't gotten down to the more subtle issues. We settled for a nice relationship but there were nagging problems that kept getting in the way of our experiencing joy and intimacy a lot of the time. As we took a closer look at our system we began to discover the very difficult patterns that had developed between us.

We had slipped into a co-dependent relationship with Margie being responsible for the emotional health of the family. She had given up important parts of herself to make everyone happy. Thinking she was being loving, she was dismayed, hurt, and angry when her efforts didn't produce appreciation and love. She had become more and more unhappy and angry. Jordan, who was raised to be taken care of, had made Margie responsible for his happiness and was in a perpetual state of muffled irritation and anger at her because he wasn't happy. When Jordan wasn't happy, it was because Margie wasn't sexual enough or funny enough or something enough.

Margie began to find her happiness outside of the relationship. She became less and less available and all four of the kids (Sheryl, Josh, Eric, and Jordan) were very unhappy and became blaming and defensive.

When the self-righteous anger and blame subsided we began to unravel the system of beliefs that was causing our unhappiness. When we finally opened to learning, each individual in the family looked at his or her part in creating the limiting system we were in. As a result, we have all been discovering more and more about ourselves—we are rediscovering the joyful parts of ourselves that became muted in our self-limiting roles; we are creating more intimacy; and we are all feeling better about ourselves and each other.

JORDAN

Margie's decision to not be around when she felt pulled at to make people happy, or when anyone was angry with her, was an act of love. She was giving each of us a gift of the truth—the truth that nobody feels good about or wants to be around someone who is unloving. When we don't let others know when we feel unloved or when we just leave unloving situations (emotionally or physically), without expressing what we're reacting to, we perpetuate a system of lies. The truth is always a gift because it creates an opportunity to learn and change. But people often don't appreciate the truth as a gift of love.

I reacted the way most people do when afraid of opening to the truth. I got angry and sought others' support as I complained about the unfairness in my situation. Have you ever heard yourself in the following dialogue: "Can you believe what she's doing?!" (A passionate description of the other's "wrong behavior" follows.)

"Really, I don't blame you for being pissed off. I wouldn't

stand for someone doing that to me."

"Yeah, she really is out of line. Look at all I've done for her and that's the thanks I get."

"I can't believe how selfish she's being."

"I don't know if I can take this. Maybe I should just find someone else who would appreciate me."

"Well, I certainly wouldn't blame you for that. You deserve it!"

The kids and I would have our family meetings and a lot of the time would be spent focused on Mom (who usually wasn't there). We self-righteously supported each other's complaints. Armed with that kind of support from my children and friends, I stayed angry, waiting for her to shape up. There was no intention to learn on anyone's part and without that we were stuck in a deteriorating situation. The more I stayed angry the more Margie wanted to be away and the more she was away the more I was angry.

We were so deeply enmeshed in our system that we needed the help of friends and therapists (some of whom we'd trained), who hadn't been caught up in the blame, to help us see the issues more clearly. As our system began to unravel, we had to learn more about co-dependence to see and understand what we had created. What a rude awakening it was to realize that we were like addicts and that we needed to accept an on-going process of recovery.

For me, the beginning of new learning was having to look at my sexual neediness and how obsessive my thinking had become. I can now see that we all have grown up with many false beliefs about sex which condition us toward sexually-related problems.

Most men have been conditioned to believe that their self-worth hinges on a woman being attracted to them. So, when a man is attracted to a woman and takes her out, getting her to have sex with him is primary. He may take her to dinner, to a movie, talk with her about areas of interest; but if the evening doesn't wind up in bed, he is often frustrated and angry. He may feel badly about himself ("If I were more interesting, successful, better looking, funnier, then she would have gone to bed with me"); he may feel used if she doesn't honor his unspoken contract ("I'll be nice to her and in return, she'll give me sex"); and he may blame her if he's too upset to sleep ("If she really cared about me she would have sex with me"). He may feel angry because she has denied him the opportunity to give his wonderful gift to her. He may even delude himself into believing that his attempt to "give" to her is altruistic.

If he gets his fix (an orgasm), he may feel happy and loving and will try to convince her how easy he is to please; and when he's pleased, see how delightful he can be. But, alas, the peaceful feelings don't last for very long before he needs another fix and if he doesn't get it, then it's her fault that he's so nasty and irritable. Doesn't that sound familiar? That's how it was for me–I was no different than any addict who seems to be content when he's got his substance, but when the effect of the drug wears off, he's plotting and thinking about how and when he'll get his next one. Denied my drug (sex), I was capable of doing all kinds of unloving things to Margie and myself.

All my life I thought that if I could get enough sex, I would feel okay about myself. A major focus in my relationship with women was to get sexual affirmation. When I wasn't happy and something was wrong, sex may not have been the cause, but I thought it would be the cure. That made Margie, as my wife and sexual partner, responsible for my happiness. If only she would initiate sex more often, be sexier outside of bed, be sexier in bed, want sex more often, then I'd be happy and we'd be happy.

Whenever I was unhappy, then, it was because she wasn't doing something right. I was often uptight with her and I couldn't understand why she wasn't turned on to me sexually. I wasn't ready to hear that her sexuality had something to do with feeling loved.

When Margie finally decided that she wasn't going to have sex with me unless she felt loving, that was the last straw. I believed that if we waited for that to happen we would never make love. And how could I ever feel good about myself if my own wife rejected me? Being trained to think in certain ways, my mind raced ahead in self-righteous anger to the thought of finding someone else to make love with. After all, I deserved it, she was wrong, and I'd show her how wrong she was. Until that happened I was forced to sleep in the same bed with a cold fish.

Night after night I'd restlessly toss and turn alternately cursing her and thinking "Here is this woman I have lusted over for twenty years. She is *beautiful.* She has a body that matches my most erotic fantasies. She's next to me in bed naked. *And I can't even touch her!* Why me? Why me?" The answer to that question has taken me on a fascinating journey of confronting my beliefs about sex and helping me to learn the truth.

The Bible says that "The truth will set you free." Nowhere in my life has this been so dramatically demonstrated than in my discovering the truth about my sexuality. The false beliefs that imprisoned me and led to a lot of my unhappiness were that I needed sex in order to: feel good about myself; sleep well at night; be loving with my wife; be faithful. Another crippling false belief was that I had the right to get my needs met, and that a woman's right to say "no" was not as important. (In other words, to invade a woman's body was no big deal.) The momentary pleasure was worth any price, even if it meant Margie might be temporarily unhappy. After all, *more* sex would cure the feeling of emptiness or distance between us.

As we went through months of very sparse sexuality, I had plenty of opportunity to discover these beliefs and test them out. One by one, they were brought into the light of truth.

When I look over these commonly held false beliefs and realize how much misery they caused us both, I feel very sad. Men have perpetuated many false beliefs about our own and women's sexuality, beliefs that have led to low self-esteem, marital problems, child abuse, rape. Even in this enlightened age, false beliefs about sex are expressed all around us.

Knowing that I don't need sex has been very liberating. Yes, I still desire to connect sexually and love our sexual experiences. When they are an expression and an outgrowth of our intimacy, they are beautiful and passionate. When we are not in an open and flowing place, my intention is now to resolve the distance rather than attempt to create a pseudo-closeness by having sex. When

Margie is not feeling sexual, we can still be affectionate and that's wonderful. Even when I get sexually aroused, there is not the urgency to complete a sexual act. Without that urgency, many options and freedoms open up to us that weren't there when there was only one outcome with which I could be happy.

At the same time I was confronting my sexual neediness, it became apparent that I was excessively dependent on Margie in other ways. One evening before I was to leave on a trip, just before drifting off to sleep I said, "I'm going to miss you." Margie replied, "Why? I haven't been very nice to you lately and we haven't been getting along very well."

I thought for a moment about the work I would be doing on my trip and the people I'd be working with and said, "You're right, I'm not going to miss you." I thought a lot that night about why I had said that and realized that in my belief system, if I really loved someone I would be miserable being away from her, since I needed her to be happy.

I woke up the next morning and talked with Margie about my realizations that love was all tied up with need. I blurted out, "But if I didn't need you, why would I be with you?" "Because we like being together and we offer each other some wonderful things," she answered.

I quickly saw how twisted my thinking had been. In fact, I realized that it is impossible to love someone or something you need for your happiness or well being. Neediness feels weak and eventually turns into resentment toward the person or thing you need. The alcoholic doesn't love alcohol any more than the compulsive eater loves food. The desperate energy of need is the antithesis of love. Yet every love song and love story teaches us the "romantic love" of neediness.

I further realized why I was always angry anytime we reunited after having been separated. I spoke of missing Margie and not being very happy during our separation and she often came back bubbling about the wonderful time she had. I became convinced that this was an indication of the fact that I loved her more than she loved me. I would get sullen and withdrawn and we

34

would usually have awful reunions.

That morning she became very excited as we talked and said, "Gee, maybe this time we can each have a wonderful time while we're apart and when we get back together we can share our excitement." What a novel thought! We kissed good-bye.

I came back happy, she shared with me the good time she had, I felt happy for her and our shared joyous intimacy created one of the best evenings of our lives.

That was the beginning of confronting one of the deepest fears and beliefs I had–that I couldn't make myself happy. I had depended on Margie, just as a child depends on a parent, to take care of me emotionally. To the outside world I'm sure I didn't look needy. I was successful and self-assured whether in business or social meetings, or on stage or television giving presentations to thousands of people. But at home I was a needy child depending on "mommy" to make me happy. Oh sure, I could entertain myself with reading, television, or work but I would be secretly waiting for the time Margie and I would spend together, especially for our sexual encounters.

Whenever I wasn't happy, I immediately thought of something Margie was or wasn't doing. She was responsible for my happiness and my unhappiness. I was preoccupied with trying to get her to be different so that I'd be happy. As she danced through the hoops I set out for her and I was happy for a while, I became even more convinced she was responsible for whatever unhappiness I was feeling. When the happiness went away, it was because she wasn't doing something right again and we became focused on fixing her. Margie, being a person who believed she was responsible for others' happiness or unhappiness (i.e., if only she could do it right another person would be happy), played the game perfectly. (She'll tell you her story later.)

What did it mean to be able to be happy on my own? What did it mean to be able to find joy in anything I was doing? I had never considered that before. To be able to do that would mean that when I was with her I'd be happy and when I was not, I'd be happy.

I realized that there were not a lot of things I did where I found that joy. I knew I had to find more of them. But the deeper issue was how to find joy in whatever I was doing. I had heard of that in some of the readings I had done in Zen philosophy.

At this point, I began to confront the meaning of God and my Higher Self. One day during this period, I went outside in our backyard to read, and the experience was not just reading to fill time, it was finding joy in reading. It was experiencing the feeling of the sun warming me and the slight breeze caressing the hair on my body. It was letting my whole being become filled with the beauty of the environment we had created and feel overwhelmed with the beauty that God had created without any help from me. It was a spectacular experience, and Margie wasn't even there. Could I do that in every moment of my life? That would be a major challenge. But I could at least start by making it happen more! The things around me didn't change, it was my beliefs that changed.

The changes were not easily accomplished. I had to test out my fear of not needing her. If we were that free, would we still have a marriage? That freedom is one of the most frightening things for couples to confront.

I came to understand how I had become dependent on Margie taking care of me emotionally. I, like most men, had been taken care of by my mother. I easily slipped into believing that she was responsible for my happiness and unhappiness. And then I grew up and got married to...guess who?

Because of our early dependence on mother, most men have a real, basic fear of women. That issue rarely gets resolved in childhood and must get resolved in our adult relationships with women. The fear began when we needed both our mothers' love and our own identities at the same time. Mother was usually the one most involved in the everyday process of trying to mold us. We needed our integrity and we needed her love. Needing her was terrifying. We developed a love-hate relationship. As I reflect on my work with men, it seems to me that men grow up with this ambivalence toward women which leads to six distinct ways of being: 1) being attracted to women we can control; 2) staying away from relationships altogether; 3) being attracted to relationships with men (these are men who become homosexual out of fear rather than the men who are genetically homosexual); 4) giving up and allowing a women to be dominant; 5) keeping a number of women available to us–not putting all our eggs in one basket; and 6) being attracted to powerful women and then getting into power struggles with them out of our fear of being controlled by them.

The last way is the pattern I had always created. I am very attracted to powerful women. But being in a relationship with one taps into my deepest fears and then up come my defenses. I used to daydream, at times, about how nice it would be to be married to Suzie Homemaker. (I had some friends who were and their lives seemed so easy.) But I have never been attracted to that kind of woman. I realized that there is something inside of me that wants to evolve out of the patterns of my past and there is no way Suzie and I could do that. My best alternative? Keep Margie and resolve the fears that get in my way of being truly powerful enough to have an equal relationship, a relationship in which I don't have to be in control to prevent being controlled. (The need to be in control always comes from the fear of being controlled. It can be hard to see, but people who seem to be controlling and powerful are actually afraid and weak.)

As I began to study spirituality, I became fascinated with those figures who were truly powerful, those people who didn't have to be controlling because they came from a place of sureness inside of themselves. The power that comes with that sureness is awesome. That's how I wanted to be. I didn't want to have to control either subtly or overtly. I wanted to be able to stay centered in any situation, no matter how my wife or my children or anyone else behaved around me.

Jesus stood out for me as a model of what I would like to become. I began to study who Jesus was. Not the Jesus that I think has been distorted to meet the ego needs of men, but the Jesus who was the model of love. The Jesus who reacted to all situations with love. I hope you, my readers, can understand and accept that I am not Christian (I'm Jewish), nor am I a born-again Christian nor am I a part of a cult like Jews for Jesus. I am just one person searching for the knowledge inside of me to be the best person I can be.

What gets in the way of that the most are my false, self-limiting beliefs. The most pervasive result of those beliefs is feeling wrong. The fear of being wrong destroys every opportunity I have to learn and change. The fear of being wrong is what keeps us all from being open to learning. In any situation, I completely lose the desire to learn when I fear that in the learning I'll find out that I'm inadequate, WRONG. Only when I take full responsibility for my life can I open to learning. When I don't take full responsibility because I fear being wrong, I get stuck focusing on Margie's part in any difficulty rather than just staying focused on myself. When responsibility means blame, I'm stuck. This has been the area of my work that has created the most profound changes, the changes that are transforming. These are changes that don't come from a decision to change, but occur from the belief changes that move me from my ego to my Higher Self.

I feel best about myself when I react with openness, caring, love. I feel alive, powerful, in control. Protected–defensive, pulled in, tight, attempting to control–I feel dead, weak, scared. It's hardest to maintain my center when I'm with Margie. It's always in our primary relationships that our biggest challenge lies. Learning what it means to be loving to myself and others and removing the blocks to that behavior is the focus of the intent to learn. I, like so many others, have put that focus far down the list of my priorities. But when I think of it, nothing is more important in life than learning to be loving, to move into the consciousness that touches everyone I meet in a positive way.

MARGIE

It took me a long time to tune in to my equal responsibility for the problems between us. After all, I prided myself on being the giver in our family. I usually went along with what people wanted and was forever there to fix up whatever problems anyone was having. On the surface that looks loving, but when I saw how often my behavior was motivated by fear and guilt and how it was neither giving others personal responsibility for their lives nor taking responsibility for myself, I felt like I was in shock.

I began to confront the price I paid for my compliance. I felt burdened with the responsibility I had taken and no matter how much I did, those around me never seemed to get enough. I felt depleted and unhappy most of the time and I didn't feel good about myself, but I was terrified to really confront the problems. If I were to be honest about how unhappy I was, Jordan and our family might fall apart. I believed I was the glue and my terror was in testing that out.

My whole identity and worth was tied up in being a caretaker, being the one who would put my needs last, coming from the belief that what I wanted wasn't important, and that I did not have the *right* to make myself happy. Being a caretaker was how I had learned to get approval from the time I was little. I believed my parents couldn't handle who I really was, that my intensity and curiosity would create situations that they couldn't handle. (I don't know if that was true but that's what I believed.) So I became a good little girl by either repressing who I was or expressing it without letting my parents know. I believed I was responsible for their happiness or unhappiness and was forever adjusting my behavior either to make them happy or keep them from becoming unhappy. I was a co-dependent, addicted to approval.

One of the deepest fears I had to test out when I wanted to break my addiction was: "The people who say they love me really don't." In other words, if I was to behave from who I really am, from my Higher Self, then others would be upset with me and withdraw their love. I had lived with that belief my whole life and it was after 20 years in my relationship with Jordan that I finally decided to test it out.

I entered my relationship with Jordan fully knowing that I was capable of doing anything I decided to tackle. I had the confidence that goes along with meeting challenges and successfully completing them. I also had those beliefs about being responsible for others and the fears that always follow. Jordan was a wonderfully sensitive man who had been, in his words, "A spectacular failure" in everything he had tried. I saw in him a wonderful human being with great "potential" and I knew that we could have a terrific life if I could help him realize it. The only flaw in my thinking was not recognizing the trap of taking responsibility for someone else.

Although Jordan blossomed, everyone else seemed to get the benefits but me. He became successful, more self-assured and an even more sensitive male. Most people loved him, but with me he was often shut down, and he often seemed to be angry with me. I believed that if only I could fix the things in me that "made him" unhappy, he would be happy and things would get better. Jordan and I colluded to make me responsible for his happiness. This was another hole in my thinking.

It became more and more clear that in giving up myself I was becoming more and more unhappy. Although I muted my enthusiasm and pursuit of new ideas, Jordan was still not satisfied and I felt like I was withering. In addition, he wasn't being any happier around me. By taking so much responsibility for his happiness I was perpetuating a belief system where he didn't have to take responsibility. By playing the game of having him be dependent on me I was partially responsible for keeping him an emotional cripple and that was not loving.

Pulling out of that system was the most terrifying thing I have ever done. My deepest fears were activated–Jordan would be angry with me and either withdraw emotionally or leave the relationship, proving that I wasn't really important to him and that he didn't really love me. This would confirm that I was unlovable and had little worth; that I was wrong (the "Martian" which he often called me when he wanted to prove that I was weird). Before I was willing to test out my beliefs, my emotional and physical health deteriorated to the point where I had to risk losing the relationship.

To gain the strength to test out my fears, I needed help from some very special people in my life. These special people helped me learn to respect my right to think and feel as I do.

I have always received a lot of criticism for the way I think and act. As an only child, my primary peer connections were with my three male cousins who definitely didn't appreciate my female ways of thinking. My grandmother and parents were very caught up in their ideas about the right way to think, feel and act and the "real me" didn't fall into those categories. Twenty-five years ago, my ideas about nutrition were criticized as kookie. I ate natural foods that were not adulterated with chemicals. As an artist, I discovered my most creative time was during the night so I often painted through the night and slept until noon. In graduate school, the subjects I wanted to paint and the colors I wanted to use were criticized by my male instructors. My thoughts and feelings seemed so out of step that I covered up who I really was and created my "good girl" persona.

I have always felt a tremendous conflict inside of me between who I really was and what others expected of me. Whenever the "unusual" part of me would surface, Jordan would become upset and we would argue. I would usually give up wanting what I wanted or doing what I wanted, but it never changed my desire. Whether it was health foods, sexual, emotional, metaphysical, or spiritual issues, we would go through months or years of battling until Jordan opened to learning from what I was feeling or thinking. That doesn't mean that he would always agree with me but he eventually gave up his need to make me wrong for my way of thinking. Because we were both willing to hang in there until we opened to learning, the process led to our both learning and growing but the cost eventually began to take its toll.

Even though I gave in a lot, I also continually brought up the subjects where we were at odds. My intent was to get Jordan to open and to change–"for his own good," of course. Most issues wound up in power struggles. I could never understand why he would get so defensive whenever I wanted to talk, until I recognized that my intent was almost always to get him to change and part of the problem was his resisting being controlled by me. I was well aware of Jordan's attempts to control me but seeing how controlling I was was a real shocker.

Trying to *get* another to change his/her behavior is always controlling. Wanting change was not the problem. Trying to create an openness between us, help him reach his potential or get his approval, was motivated by my fear of disapproval and emotional disconnection and my guilt in feeling wrong for what I want or for "making" him unhappy, not my love for either him or myself.

As I shed the weak and passive parts of me and the hard edges that I put up to protect myself, I move more into the person that I really like being. As I discover more of my true Goddess energy I am better able to really help Jordan discover more of this alienated energy within himself. We are discovering together the true possibilities within ourselves and between us.

It's becoming more and more okay to rely on my intuition and perceptions. When I am in concert with my Higher Self, I sense things that may not be obvious to others, such as unloving behavior that is being passed off as loving. (The play/movie *Nuts* is about this kind of knowing.) When I am being true to myself I often behave in ways that may touch off difficulties for others. For example, being excited and behaving with my intense enthusiasm, or passionately wanting to pursue every issue down to the bottom line, often leaves others feeling uncomfortable. Not wanting to be sexual unless I felt emotionally connected has left Jordan with many uncomfortable feelings.

The hardest things for me to resolve have been my fears and beliefs around taking responsibility for others. I have always believed that I should never do anything that upset another. If I wanted something but knew that someone else would be upset, then if I really loved that person I would give up what I wanted. After all I was strong and I could take the disappointment better than they could.

I realized that I needed to think differently. Since my feelings and behavior were never motivated by the intention to hurt another, why were my feelings or behavior wrong? What really caused others to feel hurt? When I finally took a deep look at what created feelings in myself and others, I realized that *feelings come from beliefs.* Therefore, I could never cause other people to feel a certain way, because *their beliefs* were causing *their feelings*. If a person *believed* something was wrong, he or she would get upset. If I didn't want to make love with Jordan and he got hurt, then his hurt was coming from his fears and beliefs. If I jumped up and down when I was excited and he was embarrassed, his upset was coming from his beliefs about what was "appropriate" behavior and his fears of others judging him because of my behavior. It was liberating to realize that this applied to everything that we have come to believe is the "right way" to be. As long as my intent is not to harm another person, is there any behavior that is wrong?

But what if Jordan was so upset with me that he would leave the relationship? That was something that I had to be willing to find out. I was scared to lose the relationship but I knew that I would never be happy holding myself back and had already grown to resent Jordan and the marriage. I could see that our relationship and love had been deteriorating and I wasn't willing to settle for an emotionally distant relationship.

Because my beliefs were very new and I wasn't very secure in my right to have them, I took my new found freedom with some hard self-righteousness. I now know that whenever I get hard and irritated, it's because I'm afraid that he can make me feel guilty and talk me out of my feelings. Confronting my irritation, which sometimes is seen as parentalness, has been extremely important for my growth and development. Obviously, the more secure I feel the softer I can remain. Real strength comes from knowing that it's okay to feel what I feel and want what I want.

I tested out my freedom in many areas and learned a lot from each. One of the most profound learnings has occurred in the area of sex. Both Jordan and I have been astounded about how many erroneous beliefs we have grown up with about sex. I never knew that I had the right not to be touched, let alone made love to, if I didn't want to. I was afraid that any man with whom I was involved would be upset with me if I didn't allow him to use my body. Or if he wasn't upset with me, then he might feel inadequate, uncomfortable, disappointed, and I would be responsible for that.

I felt there was something wrong with me if I didn't feel

turned on as often as Jordan. I felt there was something wrong with me for sometimes not liking to have Jordan touch me. Jordan often expressed his love for me and it was obvious that he was turned on to me and I often felt wrong in not appreciating how much he enjoyed looking at and touching my body.

It has taken a long time to appreciate and validate my sexuality which is very different from Jordan's. Neither one is wrong, we're just different. He has a greater physical need for sex than I do. My sexuality is much more connected to my emotions than his, although that has changed a great deal for him. For me, sex is the outgrowth of feeling emotionally connected and loving. I almost always need to be connected emotionally before I feel sexual. Jordan, on the other hand, opens emotionally much more easily after we make love.

It's been difficult for me to not feel guilty and wrong for not being turned on as much as men have wanted me to be. Beginning in my childhood, I've always felt I had to be on guard. It seems as though the energy of men's sexuality has always been hovering around me waiting for an opening to jump into (not a bad pun). I have rarely felt a man's genuine interest in knowing me and really caring about me. There always seemed to be an ulterior motive. I often gave in and had sex when I wasn't turned on to try to avoid a man's anger, or to please him, or to protect him from feeling bad. Sex was totally tied up with guilt and fear.

Where did my sexual feelings come from? Did I have a right to not make love if I wasn't turned on, not be touched if I didn't want to be? What would it be like if sex happened as a result of love and mutual desire rather than from neediness? I needed some time to sort through my feelings about sex to figure out what I wanted.

As I've become more aware of the good reasons I have for feeling as I do, I've realized that there are two different kinds of touch—either a giving or a taking. Sometimes I feel Jordan's touch to be coming from his true concern for me. It's a caring, nurturing touch and it feels wonderful. Other times his touch is trying to get something from me, to get me turned on, to appreciate him, to make things better, to take comfort for himself. When this is the case I feel invaded and used. I don't feel cared about because he's not caring about me he's only caring about himself. He has often said that he's doing these things for me but when he's really caring about me he would only touch me if I want to be touched and where I want to be touched. He'd be asking me how I feel and/or sensing my discomfort rather than just ignoring me and running over me.

Touch is either nurturing or taking (pulling at another for something that you want). Sex, as well, falls into these two categories. Unfortunately sex is usually either taking (using) or giving in (being used). All of our training has taught us these two ways of expressing ourselves sexually. Sex as a giving, loving experience is almost never seen and rarely appreciated.

Jordan has come to realize that a great deal of his sex drive was out of neediness rather than out of love. In his belief system was all the training which taught him that if a woman was turned on to him, then he would feel better about himself. Sex became the experience in which he felt most adequate, joyful, and in the moment. In contrast, the time leading up to making love was when he became most needy and manipulative. And that's not a turn on for me. He would usually get into bed focused on making love. I didn't feel it had anything to do with me but was only for him. He wasn't really interested in what I was thinking or feeling, he just wanted to get his needs met.

Jordan finally acknowledging his sexual neediness and opening to learning about it was an important turning point in our relationship. At some point I told him that if he ever got into bed with the thought of nurturing me rather than going for sex, that if there was any chance at all that I'd feel like making love, it would grow out of feeling his caring.

As we have both brought our sexual attitudes more in line with love, sex has become much less of a problem. There are still many unresolved feelings for both of us, so neither of us are totally satisfied with our sex life, but we're moving in that direction.

Sex is only one of the areas that has produced a tremendous amount of learning. My intuitive knowing has opened up many fertile areas. Like most women, my intuition and openness to ways of knowing other than intellectual has always been disregarded. Only recently are more and more people opening to this way of thinking and knowing.

I am very attuned to people's energy. When Jordan is shut down and silently angry, I can feel that coldness in another part of the house. In the past, when I'd offer him my perceptions he'd tell me that he wasn't shut down. He would essentially say that I was crazy. And I didn't have enough confidence in myself to know that I was right. Now I know that when I'm sensing something, I may not always label it correctly but something's going on. For example, when I feel Jordan's uptight energy I may say "You seem angry." If he says, "I'm not angry," then we're stuck. He's not open to learning and there's no place to go. If he says, "I'm not aware of feeling angry but let's take a look at what you're sensing and what I am feeling," then we can learn. I may not have labeled his feelings accurately but I'm feeling some problem in our openness or within him. If he completely denies my perception, then it's obvious that he's not open to learning and my perception that something's going on is validated. When there are truly no difficulties going on inside of him, then he is open.

I feel the difference between Jordan's sexual energy when he's needy and his energy when he's caring. I feel the difference between the energy of his openness and his closedness. I feel a completely different energy when a person is pulling at me for approval or coming from a position of real inner strength. I feel the distinctly different energy when a person is a victim or really taking personal responsibility by willing to be open to learning. I am learning to trust my perceptions and that makes some people very uncomfortable. The people who are most uncomfortable around me are those who are not open to learning. I am a person who truly loves to learn. I am excited by the challenges in learning. I welcome crisis as an opportunity to learn and I seek new challenges to increase my learning. I see that the most important purpose in life is to be loving and to learn about the blocks to learning.

I would rather learn than teach. Jordan loves to teach but

learning has been difficult for him because of all the fears he's had of being wrong. The fear of being wrong has created a great deal of defensiveness in him and made our learning less than the joy that is possible. We have learned a lot together but the process has not been fun. It can be a wonderfully joyful process when we don't have to worry about being wrong.

When we are both open to learning, the intimacy and growth that become possible are incredible. Any situation can create intimacy or distance depending upon whether we approach it with the intent to learn or the intent to protect.

A great deal of our power struggle centered around my offering Jordan my perceptions and his resisting them. Even when he told me that he wanted my perceptions, he would argue with me when I offered them and then I would feel drained and frustrated. I finally understood that the problem was that I was *still* taking responsibility for him. I realized that there was *nothing I could say or do that would make a difference*. I had said it all–there was nothing more to say. If he wanted to be aware of his intent, he would have to choose consciousness rather than rely on me to point out his intent. Letting go of feeling responsible for him knowing his intent and/or trying to change his intent has freed me enormously.

It's not fun being around people who don't want to learn. I feel bored a lot with conversation and situations where there is no newness. I don't feel at all judgmental of those people who are not open to learning, but I choose to structure my life around the things that really excite me.

Many interesting and challenging things have resulted in our life as a result of my respecting my right to follow my own path. Jordan and I have begun to do many more things separately. He does most of the teaching and a lot of the writing. I do more therapy and spend a great deal more time pursuing my art, as well as writing separately from him. Art has become an important vehicle for me to delve more deeply into my femininity. Being alone is much more important to me than it is to him. I've only recently come to respect my need to be alone. Jordan has had to find ways to make himself happy in the face of our not being as together as we were during the first twenty-three years of our marriage.

This is not the form that Jordan has had for how a marriage should be. He used to spend a great deal of energy trying to make me fit into his ideals. He has come to respect me as an individual and has had a choice: he could leave this marriage and find someone who was closer to his ideal or, if he chose to stay and learn whether he could find happiness within this form. This has been quite a challenge for both of us. I have a great deal of respect for what Jordan has had to go through. He decided to learn from the form he has been presented rather than try to get his way. I've had to risk losing this marriage and my family, which have been so important to me, to pursue finally coming into harmony with my true self.

We are certainly not out of the woods. The road has been very rocky but we're each much happier within ourselves, feeling stronger, more alive, more in harmony and integrity with who we really are. The struggle to change a deeply ingrained addictive system could not have been accomplished without a great deal of help. Our friends, those therapists and writers who have helped us through their own willingness to struggle, and our spiritual teachers have been invaluable.

We must not forget one other important source of our growth–God. Being very non-religious people for most of our lives, both of us have found strength in God. Our God may be different from yours, but any way that we can tap into the universal truth is necessary if we are to transcend the pitfalls created by human beings. To understand what it means to turn our lives over to our Higher Selves has been essential for us.

BOTH OF US

JORDAN: We're learning to have faith. If I get into learning all there is to learn about me–why do I want what I want; what is the issue between us; are we in a power struggle–and Margie is learning about herself, out of that learning we will be changed. In the process of learning about our fears and beliefs, we are changed. As we change, the problem that we started out talking about will be changed and we will reach a mutually satisfying resolution. To understand what it means to be in a process is a very foreign concept to Westerners because we are very solution oriented. We don't have faith that if we just open to learning, we'll find resolution. Instead, we try to find solutions or we go to people who tell us what to do, calling them on the radio to be told in six minutes how to solve our problems. That's going right to solution rather that being in a process of growth and learning.

MARGIE: Sometimes, if there is openness and we are not in a power struggle, things can get resolved very quickly. The thing that keeps people from finding the resolutions quickly is the power struggle, trying to be right. We get into a win/lose, right/wrong interaction and are not open to learning. When we are in those kinds of interactions, we don't care about what the other person wants and you can't reach resolution without caring. However, if I really care about what he wants and I really want him to be happy and he cares about what I want and really wants me to be happy, we are going to resolve this issue really easily. But if I say "Well I got to stick to my guns. I don't want to be controlled" and he's doing the same thing and he's saying "I gotta win" and I'm saying "I gotta win," there is no way of resolving this issue.

JORDAN: Now, there are people who really love the process of learning and that is a major part of their lives. Margie is that kind of person. That is what she lives for. That is all that is important to her. I've been the kind of person who has opened to learning when I'm hit over the head and I have to do it. I've gone kicking and screaming. (There are those people who don't open to learning even if you do hit them over the head.) What I've needed to look at is why it has to come to crisis, what gets in the way of my really seeing the importance and the excitement of learning in any situation around me. I now know what it is. It's the fear of being wrong, a major fear from which I'm in the process of recovering.

MARGIE: Two people connect only when both people are in the intention to learn. Any two people who are open to learning will create an intimate connection. Anytime one person is open to learning and the other is not, there is no way to intimately connect. What I want in my life is to be with people who really want to learn. There are a lot of women to whom learning is the most important thing. There are a lot of men who are so afraid of being wrong because of how they've been brought up (they have to be right, they have to know everything, they can't learn from a woman, etc.) that they are afraid to be in that process.

JORDAN: True, men have been brought up to see doing as important, while women are much more able to just be, be open to the process. That's totally foreign to the way men have been raised, because our orientation is to do, and to be successful, and to create in that way. So what often happens is that women complain, "With my women friends, we can sit and talk and we connect and we can go on and on. But with my guy, there's a wall there and I don't know what the problem is." The problem is that he is afraid of the process, he is afraid of being open. It's not always the guy; very often the woman also is afraid of being open to learning within the relationship.

Outside of their families, women seem to be more open to learning. But inside their relationships, when it comes down to "What am I doing in this relationship, that's creating my own unhappiness?" then the blocks come up for women as well.

MARGIE: One of the major dilemmas that we see is that men want to connect sexually. Women can't connect sexually until they connect emotionally. Women say "I need to be open, I need to share, I need to share my feelings, I need to connect." Men are saying, "But we never make love." And they are not getting that the connection has to happen first on the emotional-spiritual level before the sexual gets tapped into. I think that what men are going to have to do is recognize that they are afraid of being open and instead of saying "Oh, why do I have to be open all the time," they need to learn to deal with their fears of being open.

JORDAN: I don't know that I will ever get to the point where the process of being open to learning is as exciting to me as it is to Margie. So it may never be equal. Many men complain, "What do you do with a woman who *always* wants to explore? How do you find the balance?" The balance comes when we learn more of the time. I don't think that in order to be intimate and to have what we can have between us that we need to be in the same place all of the time, but we need to be in that place more of the time. Then if she needs more, she can get her needs met with other people. But unless we have this a good part of the time between us, we aren't going to have the wonderful things that can happen from an intimate connection.

MARGIE: But you see, I don't even need to be in the process of learning all the time. That is not the issue. What I need is the energy of the openness. Just the *willingness* to be there when it's appropriate, and not run up against the wall. When the wall is there, there is no intimacy. I don't like to sit and process and learn all the time. I like to have fun and play. But that doesn't happen if there is a wall. It only happens when that energy is there, the energy of the openness.

JORDAN: That seems to me the best answer. It isn't how much of the time we do it, it's whether there is the openness to do it and the attitude of willingness. If the energy there is fear, that closedness is the barrier that is getting in the way.

MARGIE: When two people are open, they don't have to process very much at all. They process because they are not open and have to find out why they are not. Once they are open, then they can have fun and play and really *make love* and do all those wonderful things.

51

JORDAN: So our task is admittedly a very challenging one. It's as if we're going on blind faith. Some of you may be thinking, "They're saying that if we do this, something wonderful is going to happen, but I've never had it so I don't even know what that feels like." But we know that it does happen. We've had enough experience to know that when that openness is there between us, that energy between us is something really special. What follows, the joy and sexuality, is really special. We would define it as a spiritual connection.

This process is teaching us what it means to be truly loving to ourselves and to others. It has deepened our commitment to discovering what it will take to bring about peace within ourselves and our families and finally, peace on our planet. We hope you are moved to join us.

INTRODUCTION TO SECTION II

The remainder of this workbook is designed to help you learn how to learn from conflicts. Since conflict occurs in all relationships, relationships are obviously a most important vehicle in your personal growth. The exercises are designed to be used for conflicts with anyone who is presently in your life or has been in your life, living or dead. You can learn from conflicts in adult love relationships (heterosexual or homosexual), relationships with your parents, children, employers, employees, business partners and clients, friends, relatives and even with yourself.

The exercises will give you the opportunity to learn about yourself on a very deep level and can be used over and over again to continually deepen your learning. This workbook, like our Intention Training Workshop, is probably different from any other workbook you may have used because each exercise is related to a concept about learning. Therefore, rather than a series of exercises strung together, each one is related to the intention to learn from a conflict.

Chapter 3–LOVING BEHAVIOR contains exercises for beginning to think about and look for loving behavior. This thinking is the unusual and crucial shift in consciousness that will transform your life.

Chapter 4–FORMATS FOR LEARNING contains formats for exploration to help you remove the blocks to being a more loving person. You can use these formats any time you're open to learning from your conflicts. The formats will help you focus on the questions you can ask yourself over and over again to find the answers to what's causing your unhappiness and to find the way out of that unhappiness. *All of the exercises in this book are designed to help you use these formats.*

When you are stuck in your protections, the exercises in Chapter 5–MOVING FROM PROTECTION TO LEARNING are designed to help you move out of your protections into an openness to learning.

The awareness of what you do in a conflict and the consequences that follow from your behavior are important parts of your motivation to change. Chapter 6–PROTECTIONS AND CONSEQUENCES contains many exercises to deepen your learning about protections and their consequences.

Being open to learning means being open to learning about the fears that are in the way of your being open to learning. Chapter 7–ACKNOWLEDGING AND RESPECTING FEAR contains the exercises that are designed to help you understand your fears, the first step in moving through them.

There are three healing exercises in Chapter 8–HEALING. Two of these exercises are much longer and more complex than the others but will be well worth your time and effort. Healing the wounds from your past is invaluable in unwrapping protective coverings.

Chapter 9–CONTINUING THE PROCESS contains ideas for learning with other people, by both helping others and receiving help from others. Other resources are also included for your continued learning.

USING THE SELF-LIMITING BELIEFS CHECKLISTS

We have included many Self-Limiting Beliefs Checklists. These will be central to your learning. We use the term "self-limiting" for any belief that limits the expression and development of your potential. We are forever grateful to Wayne Dyer for popularizing this idea in *Your Erroneous Zones*. We use "erroneous", "false" and "self-limiting" interchangeably.

A belief is self-limiting and erroneous if it:

1)   keeps you from feeling good about yourself, happy, satisfied, successful;

2)   creates *any* negative feelings–fear, doubt, pain,

depression, unhappiness, anxiety or guilt;

3)   diminishes self-esteem, self-worth, aliveness;

4)   makes you feel wrong, bad, inadequate.

Non-limiting beliefs are those which:

1)   increase the quality of your life;

2)   increase your joy, happiness, self-esteem, dignity, lovability, health, feelings of fullness and aliveness;

3)   help you meet life with positive appreciation.

Any time you are in pain of any sort, including anxiety and tension, you are operating from an erroneous belief. If you were not operating from that belief, you would not be in pain. And so, any time you are in pain, it is possible to use that pain as an opportunity to learn. You could say, "What is the belief that I'm operating from that is bringing about this pain?" Obviously, if you are unwilling to feel your pain, if you are protected, you can't utilize your pain to learn, and you will just keep doing the very things that bring about the pain. We're including in our definition of pain the state of being upset. Any time you're upset, any time you're not feeling joyful, know that there is a self-limiting belief causing it.

On each list, check off the ones that you believe even a little bit. For example, your intellect may tell you that the belief "Women are not as intelligent as men" is not true, but if any part of you believes that, then check it. You can use these checklists to better understand your behavior and feelings. Each checklist contains only a portion of the self-limiting beliefs in any area. If you become aware of beliefs that are not on the lists, be sure to add them and we'd appreciate your sharing them with us. Each belief can be the subject of an exploration.

SHARINGS

At various places in the workbook, we have included conversations. These are sharings from Intention Training workshop participants during the workshop, along with our responses. We have included them where we thought it might help you become more aware of your thoughts and feelings.

TOGETHER OR ALONE

Most of the exercises in this workbook are designed to be done alone so that you can do your learning without another person being involved. Since almost every relationship problem is a result of a system created by two or more people, it only takes one person to break the system.

Some of the exercises can be done either alone or with another person and there are two sets of instructions for those. There are a few exercises that can only be done with another person, but don't let that concern you. You can save them until you develop a friendship that feels safe enough to work together.

When we refer to your "partner," that's your partner for the exercise. This could be anyone with whom you feel comfortable.

In doing exercises with another person, it's important that you monitor your intention. It's very easy when working with a "significant other" to slip into being focused on getting that person to see things.

It's also important to follow the instructions for each exercise. We may suggest you do an exercise for ten minutes because as you go through it, deeper learning will be touched off. People often run out of things to say after about three or four minutes, and the fear that they won't be able to come up with anything more to say can raise a barrier to learning. If you start discussing the exercise or analyzing it or each other, you will miss the opportunity to go deeper into the exercise and the learning. The ego is very adept at enticing you into intellectual discussions which take you away from the deep learning that can occur on an emotional level. Of course, you will also find that you can enhance your learning by tailoring some exercises to your own particular needs. There is no single "right" way. Find the way that maximizes your learning.

CREATING THE OPTIMAL ENVIRONMENT

Before doing any exercise, check to see if it is the right time and place for you to do the exercise. Create a space where you will be free of any intrusions from people, noises or other demands from the outside world. The desire to look into yourself and your past exerience with a gentle and caring intention is a good beginning, but you also need to have the freedom to do your exploration without being interrupted. Also make sure you really want to do this learning. There is a right time and place for you. Is this it? If so, let's go forward.

FAITH

When you have come to the edge
of all the light you know,

And are about to step off
into the darkness of the unknown,

Faith is knowing
one of two things will happen:

There will be something solid to stand on,
or you will be taught how to fly.

–Anonymous

CHAPTER

·3·

LOVING BEHAVIOR

Finding the loving behavior in a conflict will not be easy, since you haven't been taught to think in these terms. Almost all of your reactions in a conflict have probably been unloving. If beliefs and fears of your ego were not in the way, loving behavior would flow naturally from your Higher Self. But that is not how we've all grown up.

Behavior motivated by love, as modeled by Jesus, Gandhi, Buddha, Martin Luther King, Mother Theresa and Rabbi Hillel, is the exact opposite of the behavior modeled by the "heroes" of our current society, the people who will do anything to "win"–business executives, athletes, movie tough guys. Loving behavior is the exact opposite of what we've seen in the world and in our homes. It is people reacting openly rather than protectively and defensively. That is real power.

The following pages contain a synopsis of how to determine if your behavior is loving or not. We suggest that you xerox it and keep it where you can refer to it frequently.

DEFINITION OF LOVING BEHAVIOR

Loving behavior nurtures your own and others' emotional and spiritual growth, promotes personal responsibility and increases your self-esteem.

It is behavior that is:

Honest to yourself about yourself.
Nonjudgmental of yourself and others.
Harmonious with your Higher Self (rather than with your ego).
Integrious (Our own word which means "behaving with integrity").
Never invested in the outcome of an action

It is the behavior that leaves you feeling:

An inner peace	Joyful	God-like
Unique, special	Lovable	Soft and strong
In control of yourself		

It is not the behavior that leaves you feeling:

Tense, anxious	Angry	Weak
Scared, unsure	Rigid	Blaming
Righteous, justified	Victimized	Stagnant

Unloving behavior is any attempt to:

Avoid personal responsibility by giving in or shutting down.
Take responsibility for others.
Get others to change.
Make others wrong.
Get others to give themselves up or doubt themselves.
Establish power over others.

Loving behavior:

Makes you feel the best about you–that you're adequate and worthwhile.
Is not motivated by fear or guilt.
Is not the safe, habitual path of least resistance, the rut you've fallen into–rescuer, rescued; taking care of, being taken care of.
Will often feel like the most difficult choice.
Will often challenge deeply held beliefs and fears.

DEFINITION OF LOVING BEHAVIOR (Cont'd)

> Involves the risk that those who want you to take responsibility for their behavior, or want to control you, will not appreciate your efforts.
> May be unfamiliar, 180 degrees from what you have been doing, rather than a variation on the theme you've been using to gain approval or avoid disapproval (your own or others').

Behavior which nurtures your own emotional and spiritual growth always nurtures the emotional and spiritual growth of others. It means caring and understanding without giving yourSelf up. It gives others the true gift of love–the opportunity to look honestly at themselves and to take personal responsibility.

The intent of unloving behavior is to GET something: approval, love, affirmation, connection, appreciation, safety, recognition, caring, attention, more communication, a response, change.

The intent of loving behavior is to GIVE. There are no strings, conditions or expectations attached.

The key to knowing whether or not your behavior is loving is how you wind up feeling about yourself and the consequences that result from your behavior. Loving behavior is the best that is within you.

Should another person also respond with love, intimacy will occur. Since you can't have control over how another chooses to react, there's never any guarantee. But there is a guarantee when you respond protectively: *There will be no intimacy.*

Your focus can always be inward, taking responsibility for your own growth and joy. Loving behavior is Selfish rather than selfish. Behavior that comes from the ego is selfish; it is only concerned with getting others to give to you and to love you, rather than giving to yourself and others. When behavior comes from the Higher Self, it is Selfish.

This definition of loving behavior may have triggered many, many erroneous or self-limiting beliefs.

THE INTENT TO LEARN IS ALWAYS LOVING.

EXERCISE 1–SELF-LIMITING BELIEFS THAT GET IN THE WAY OF LOVING BEHAVIOR

The following are some of the most basic and important self-limiting beliefs. They are the fears/beliefs that are obstacles to your behaving in a loving manner. Check off the ones that apply to you. You can come back to them over and over again, using them to touch off your deepest philosophical and spiritual learning. A format for challenging beliefs can be found on page 94.

____ If I'm open to listening and learning, I will get talked out of my own views and feelings.

____ If I'm open to learning, I will find out that I'm unlovable/ inadequate.

____ If I'm open to learning, I will get blamed for someone else's unhappiness and then I will have to change to make them happy.

____ I can't make myself happy if someone around me is protecting him/herself.

____ If I forgive the people who hurt me, they will just keep hurting me.

____ If I forgive myself, then I will continue to do the things that hurt myself and others.

____ If I'm soft and open, people will see me as weak and will lose respect for me.

____ If I'm open and trusting, I'll get sucked in and duped. Then people will think I'm stupid and reject me.

____ I can't handle rejection. I can't handle the pain.

____ Even if I open to my pain, nothing will change, so why bother?

EXERCISE 2–FINDING YOUR HIGHER SELF

Loving behavior is always loving to yourself. But unless you understand the difference between the ego and the Higher Self, it's possible to use that statement to support your ego-centered behavior. Many people have done this with disastrous results. Being loving to your ego self will never make you happy or create much joy or love in your life. That behavior is selfish, self-centered, pinched in–the opposite of loving. Taking care of your Higher Self is Selfish. It leaves you feeling a sense of being at peace with yourSelf, at one with yourSelf. It is real inner strength. It is the behavior that, in the face of a conflict, makes you feel secure enough to open. It is the behavior that increases your Self-esteem and makes you feel better about who you are. It makes you feel stronger rather than weaker. It is not the false strength that comes sometimes when people delude themselves into thinking they feel stronger because they win–beating others emotionally or physically. That just makes their egos stronger. So in order to understand what it means to "take care of yourSelf," it is essential that you understand which self you are taking care of.*

It is important to recognize times when you've been in harmony with your Higher Self and remember how you felt. All of us have, at times, been in harmony with our Higher Selves. The problem is that those times are so unique and infrequent (relative to our ordinary experience), that many of us don't have a readily available memory of this quality of being. We also tend to dismiss those experiences as being accidental or certainly not available to us on a regular and easily accessible basis. But this quality of being is available to you on a far greater scale and ease than you would believe. Furthermore, we have found that to the degree you recover

*For our workshop, we have created a thirteen minute visualization tape to help people make contact with their Higher Self. The tape is also one of the techniques we will discuss in Chapter 6 for moving from a protective intention to the intent to learn. The tape is available should you wish to purchase it. Information on how to obtain it is in the back of this book.

your memory of those times when you have been operating from your Higher Self, you strengthen to the same degree your ability to recreate that quality of experience in the here and now or whenever you choose.

In *How Can I Help?*, Ram Dass and Paul Gorman describe experiences of being in the Higher Self:

> "So we look for and cherish those experiences in which we feel ourselves connected to all things in the universe.
>
> Out under the stars, stretching to encompass notions of distance and galaxies, "light years," until the mind just boggles and goes "tilt"–and suddenly your sense of specialness or separateness is replaced by a feeling of identity with the all inclusive immensity of the universe.
>
> Listening to a Bach chorale and feeling transported into a sense of order and harmony far beyond the music itself.
>
> Harvesting the garden, smiling as you remember the spring planting, and appreciating the lawfulness of fruition in nature, the same life energy in you.
>
> Making love, when you suddenly merge with someone very dear; two become one and you somehow feel more truly yourself than you ever had before.
>
> Or in service itself–comforting a crying child, reassuring a frightened patient, bringing a glass of water to a bedridden elder–when you feel yourself to be a vehicle of kindness, an instrument of love. There's more to the deed than the doer and what's been done. You yourself feel transformed and connected to a deeper sense of identity."

The following poem, written by Jordan, was an important step in his understanding of his Higher Self and will serve to illustrate the experience we're describing.

WHERE IS GOD?

I have always looked for a sign of the presence of God
Was God here today?

Before the sun broke, I did
Into gales of laughter.
Bodies entwined, we giggled over my funny dream.
Was God there?

The jammed morning freeway leads to a re-decision.
The parting clouds along the coastline reveal
The majesty of a glistening ocean caressing newly washed cliffs
Was God there?

A stopped afternoon freeway provides another opportunity.
A twisting deserted mountain road through a magical forest
Accentuated by rain, mystified by fog.
Was God there?

Racing around curves, not in control, my body tenses.
Faith replaces anxiety and nature's magnificence fills me.
Hauntingly beautiful music enters and tears well.
Was God there?

You ask what I'm feeling and the dam overflows,
Let go of fear and hardness, stay open,
Go home and learn to meditate in Times Square.
Was God there?

I turn to look at you and
An irridescent rainbow frames a moon-faced Buddha
I experience a new meaning of love.
Was God there?

At dusk, alone, I walk the beach, combing debris from the storm.
Two sparkling pieces of driftwood jump at me.
Each different, yet perfect for each of my teachers, each of my loves.
Was God there?

I am filled with peace.
God was here. God is here.

EXERCISE 2–FORMAT FOR FINDING YOUR HIGHER SELF

The recovering of your memory, and therefore of your ability to come from your Higher Self, begins with the identification of a particular time, place and situation in which you felt most truly fulfilled and at peace with yourself in the world. The following exercise will assist you in recovering your memory. You will need a tape recorder for this exercise.

PART 1

Allow yourself to relax your body and your thoughts. You may want to use some deep breathing as you rest in a comfortable sitting position to allow yourself to open to your experience and your Higher Self. Carry on this relaxation for one or two minutes before proceeding. If you have a relaxation tape that you like to listen to, this is a good time to put it on for a few minutes.

PART 2

When you feel yourself relaxed and open, answer the following question:

> "What is the best example in my life of a time when I felt fulfilled, happy, and at peace with myself?"

Allow yourself to recall your best example, not a perfect example. Be specific about where you were, what you were doing, who you were with (if there was anyone there) and when it occurred.

Example: One day during the summer of 1982, I was walking on the beach with my five-year-old son in the late afternoon, as we talked about how big the ocean was.

Allow yourself to recreate your special memory in your imagination. It may help to keep your eyes closed as you do this. Let yourself really feel and experience all the parts of your experience. What were you thinking? How did your body feel? What emotions did you have? What did you see? What did you hear? Allow yourself to be there once again, feeling fulfilled, happy and at peace with yourself. Stay with this experience for at least one minute, drinking it in, seeing, feeling, tasting, smelling and hearing all that you can remember of those moments of your greatest fulfillment.

EXERCISE 2–FORMAT FOR FINDING YOUR HIGHER SELF
(Cont'd)

PART 3

Into your tape recorder speak out loud the words and phrases that feel just right in capturing what your experience was in this very special time. You will be able to find the words that fit the experience, that feel just right as you speak them. Allow yourself as you speak to remain in touch with your memory of this time. Allow the words to deepen your experience of that time. Allow yourself to discover new depths, new dimensions of this time of fulfillment. Pause occasionally and use these quiet moments to go deeper into the experience, to remember more and more about that special time.

There will be a point when you feel complete, when you feel that you have described your experience of fulfillment for now. When you reach this point, allow yourself to pause once again.

PART 4

Ask yourself:

"What is another example of a time when I experienced real fulfillment?" and repeat the process in part 3.

PART 5

Repeat this process at least three times (or more if it feels right for you). Then stop, rewind the tape and replay yourself speaking to yourself about your experiences of fulfillment. Know that you are beginning to hear the voice of your Higher Self speaking. Listen deeply. While listening make notes of the highlights of what you have said.

PART 6

Now go back and look for the patterns in what you have experienced. See what words or phrases seem to summarize and capture the essentials of your experience of fulfillment. Write these words and phrases in whatever style feels right for you.

PART 7

Once again, from a relaxed and open place, allow yourself to experience the essence of what you have identified as the experience of being really fulfilled. As you experience that fulfillment here and now, know that you are operating from your Higher Self.

Recognize that this is what you say is true fulfillment for you. And now, is there *anything* that is more important or that you value more than this

EXERCISE 2–FORMAT FOR FINDING YOUR HIGHER SELF
(Cont'd)

experience? Ask yourself, "What is it that I really want in my life?" Recognize that this fulfillment is what you are committed to. This commitment requires no effort and no further incentive. This is what your life is all about.

PART 8
If it feels right for you, you may now want to proceed gently, and we emphasize gently, to frame in some words that feel right as a statement of your life purpose. If this is the right time to do this, take a few moments to write this purpose. Keep it to ten to twenty words, the fewer the better. Again, don't force this; if it is time for this to happen, it will happen relatively easily. Otherwise, save this for another time. When your life purpose has emerged, it will become your personal affirmation, your personal prayer, the mantra from your Higher Self. The speaking of these sacred words are both a celebration of your Higher Self as well as a pathway back to that centered state.

PART 9
You can now ask yourself a series of questions:

1. How much of the time would I like to be operating in this state of fulfillment, in my Higher Self?

2. How much of the time, up to this time in my life, have I experienced my Higher Self?

3. How much of the time have I recognized the depth of my commitment to operating out of my Higher Self?

4. From this point on, how much of the time am I committed to living in my Higher Self?

Know that your word is sacred. You are determining the quality of your life in each moment from now on.

(We give a special thanks and acknowledgement to Doug Kruschke who created this exercise. Doug is president of In Synergy, a firm in Santa Monica, California specializing in working with corporate executives who are seeking to integrate a large vision of their own and their employees fulfillment with the continued success of their organizations.)

EXERCISE 3–TAKING RESPONSIBILITY

Loving behavior is personally responsible behavior. Understanding personal responsibility is sometimes facilitated by starting at the opposite end–being a victim. Being a victim is certainly not taking responsibility or being loving, but there is a part of you that wants to be a victim. It's important not to deny that part but to acknowledge and accept it. One way to work with your victim feelings is to get into them as fully as possible, even to exaggerate them. You make yourself a victim when you believe you can't see any way to make yourself happy. You feel helpless, stuck, waiting for another to change before you can be happy.

EXERCISE 3A-THE WAYS YOU BELIEVE YOURSELF TO BE A VICTIM

Here are a few examples of some typical victim statements.

- If the kids helped around the house, I wouldn't feel so hassled.
- If only my spouse were less angry, then I could open up.
- If only my spouse listened to me, then we could be close.
- If my spouse were more sexual, then I could feel better about my body.
- It's men's fault that marriages fall apart.
- It's my parent's fault that I'm so resistant.
- It's my parent's fault that I'm so compliant.
- If I didn't have such a rotten childhood, I wouldn't be so unhappy.
- If my father was a better role model, I'd be more emotional.
- If my boss was not so critical, I would be more productive.

Take a clean piece of paper and make a list of your own. Keep them in a place where you can add to them whenever you come across new ones. When you set your mind to recognizing these beliefs, they will probably come up often.

EXERCISE 3B–FINDING THE LOVING BEHAVIOR

In any conflict you have two levels of responsibility: 1) Your part in setting up the conflict; and 2) How you react to the conflict.

You have a part in setting up almost every unhappy situation in your life. So an important first step in finding the loving behavior is to discover your unloving behavior–how you set up the unhappy situation you are in. There are situations that you may not have set up–the family you were born into; a person hitting you with an automobile while you were parked; an airplane crash that kills a loved one. There are some people who believe that on a metaphysical level even those seemingly random situations are choices, and you are responsible for creating them. We don't know it this is true. For these exercises, use the situations in which you definitely had a part. These are situations like: your child lying to you; your girlfriend cheating on you; an argument that occurred after you criticized your husband, wife, business partner or parent.

There is no question, however, about the other level of responsibility–*how you react to any given situation.* One of the most difficult things for people to accept is the responsibility for their reactions. Since not everyone reacts the same way to the same set of circumstances, it seems obvious that something inside each of us determines how we react. That something is your beliefs. You may not be able to change the actual situation, but you can change the effect it's having on you.

There are many stirring examples of this possibility. Viktor Frankl's *Man's Search For Meaning*, in particular, details with stunning impact how differently his various fellow prisoners reacted to being incarcerated in a concentration camp during World War II. When you are powerless to change something, writes Frankl, you are challenged to change the way you think about it.

As with everything else you always have two choices: to react protectively or to open and react lovingly. This exercise, in two parts, is designed to put you in touch with your choices and their consequences. This is such an important concept that we have included much more discussion than you'll find in any other exercise. Please read the whole exercise, including the discussion, before doing either Part 1 or 2.

PART 1 – Taking personal responsibility for a conflict

1. When do you or did you feel like a victim?

    (Preferably pick a situation you're still in. If you can't think of one, then pick a past incident. This could be any ongoing conflict, especially those where you feel yourself to be in a power struggle. Examples might be: your child has been lying to you; your mate doesn't seem very interested in being sexual with you; you've caught your mate cheating on you; you have an employee who's not performing up to his/her previous standards.)

2. How are you responsible for causing the initial incident?

3. Describe your behavior in the conflict. How are you responsible for creating the interaction and the consequences?

Example: The incident was when I walked in on my girlfriend while she was in bed with another guy. I guess my responsibility was that I didn't call first, and also there must have been something going on between us that led her to do that and not to tell me about it but I'm not sure what that was. It's hard for me to know how I was responsible for causing the initial incident. Maybe I wasn't totally honest.

The incident that followed was awful. We had a big fight. I don't think I've ever been so angry. I can still remember shaking with fear and anger. I finally left telling her I never wanted to see her again. I went home feeling self-righteous but very alone. We did get back together, but it was never the same. I guess she felt attacked by my anger and blame and she got very defensive. I was just as much part of the insults and threats that followed as she was.

PART 2 – Finding the loving response in a conflict

1. Using the situation you described in Part 1, think about what you could have done or could now do that would be loving and complete the following statement:
    "A reaction that is loving and personally responsible is............"

Example: Instead of getting angry I could have then or could now want to learn about my part in creating this situation. Had I given the message that I would not tolerate that kind of behavior, thereby setting up a situation where she might go behind my back? Were there things going on between us that we had not confronted?

I could learn about why I get angry and the consequences of that behavior. I could care enough to be concerned about her. I could learn about the very good reasons she must have for behaving as she did, both the sleeping with the other guy and in the interactions that followed. I could explore and learn about my expectations and beliefs about sexual fidelity and about relationships.

Does that sound difficult to do? You're right, it is. We never said loving behavior was going to be easy. None of us are used to it and it flies in the face of how we've learned to be. The exercises in Chapter 4–Formats For Learning are designed to help you expand your understanding of your current behavior and create behavior which is more loving.

A good place to start is to remember that the *intention to learn will always be loving.* To want to learn about yourself and to want to understand the very good reasons the other person has for her behavior is loving in itself and will lead to other loving behaviors.

Don't mistake a loving response with giving yourself up. That's never loving, nor is taking responsibility for others–that is, doing for others what they can do for themselves or trying to "fix" them or offering them awarenesses that they haven't asked for or don't want. When you take responsibility for another's exploration, you may be avoiding your own.

Discussion from the workshop

SHARING: I'm having trouble with this. Say you're trying to learn about somebody. You have all the best intentions to understand her position and she sticks with her position. Then you're in an argument situation with both sides trying to explain how they feel and neither side believing the other and you're both trying to learn. Then what?

MARGIE: You're not trying to learn. Explanations are not the intention to learn. That is what is subtle about this. Lots of times you think you want to learn, but if you're explaining, if you have to be right, if you're having to win, if you're having to have your way, there is no intention to learn.

SHARING: What if you don't need to be right, what if you just don't want to be criticized?

MARGIE: If the need to protect yourself against being criticized is the most important thing, then you are still closed to learning. You have to be willing to be criticized. In order to learn, you have to be willing to have all the bad things happen that you are afraid of. You have to be willing to be criticized, willing to be blamed, willing to be seen in the wrong, willing to be seen in some way you don't want to be seen. Otherwise, you can't learn. That is why it's so hard.

SHARING: When you accept that you've heard it all, you've taken the criticism and considered whether or not you can learn something from it, and you're open to experiencing the pain of whatever it is you're being called, then what do you do?

MARGIE: If somebody is intent on putting you down and criticizing you, and that person is not open to learning about why she needs to do that, then you need to ask what would loving action you should take for yourself. For me, being with somebody whose intent is to criticize me is not a loving thing. So one loving response would be to say "You know, when you want to talk openly and explore, let's do that. But if what you want to do is criticize me, then I don't want to be around you." I have explored and found out that for me, the loving behavior is not to be around somebody who is critical. I don't like it. It feels lousy.

JORDAN: Do you see that it is not loving to yourself to stay in a situation where the other person's intent is just to criticize you? Now you might stay in it long enough to see if there is any validity to the criticism and what you can learn from that. But once you've done that, to just stay in it and just be in a situation where essentially you are being beaten up emotionally is not loving to yourself.

Most of us don't even recognize that we have the option to leave. This comes from the time when we were little and our parents may have abused us, emotionally or physically. Leaving the room would have caused even more abuse, so we had to stay and take it. As adults, we often act as if we were five years old and don't know that we have the right to go to another room or for a drive in the car in order to detach from a situation. You don't have to be in a situation in which you are being beaten emotionally or physically. There are other options besides just "taking it" or trying to get the other person to stop. You don't have to try to get the other person to stop. That's your attempt to try to out-control her, and then you are in a power struggle. That may be what you need to learn.

So if you're not going to have control over the other person, what else can you do? Maybe there is only one loving option–to leave for a while. That's a hard option. Very often, people don't leave until they get angry. They have to wait until they can justify such drastic action and then they leave blaming the other person for their anger. That is another protection. The loving behavior is to know that you ALWAYS have the right to leave, to say without anger: "I don't like doing this right now; this is not feeling good. If you want to learn, if you want to learn together, I'd like to do that, but I don't want to be in this abusive situation and I'm going to leave. I'll be back later and if you want to talk then, I'd like that. But if you want to go through this same kind of interaction again, I'll leave again."

Taking care of yourself with anger is an ego behavior. *Taking care of yourself without blame is the behavior that will leave you balanced and feeling best about yourself.*

MARGIE: So when people say things like "You're hurting me" as a criticism, they're not open to learning about their hurt, they are just wanting to make someone else wrong. They're blaming another for their feelings. If you want to learn from your feelings, there is a format for doing that. (Page 97) Feelings are very important to learn from and we often don't take that opportunity. When you say, "I'm hurt. You're hurting me. I'm going to tell you my feelings," you aren't open to learning. Emotions are a key, a sign saying "Look inside! There's a belief here. There's something to learn here." You can learn about that feeling's underlying beliefs, where the feeling comes from, what it's about. You can ask, "What is my lesson here? What do I need to learn?"

When the other person's intent is to learn about her feelings, it is loving to help her. If she wants help, she'll enlist your help. "Would you help me to learn about this feeling that I'm having?" But if she's only saying "I want to tell you my feelings," she is not open to learning and she's not enlisting your help becoming open, she just wants to have control over you. So being a part of that is not loving.

If somebody says "You're hurting my feelings," a loving response is always to look at yourself and see what your intention is. In addition, a loving response would be to say, "Why do you believe that? What would I want to do that for? And why do you believe that it is possible for me to do that to you?" If she is willing to look at that, if she is willing to move into the intention to learn, then it would be loving to be there and to help her. But if she just says, "Because you are. You are hurting my feelings because you're never around. You're hurting my feelings because...." Whatever it is, there is no point in the interaction. At that point, a loving response would be, "I don't like being blamed for whatever you are feeling and when you are willing to explore, let me know."

SHARING: I'm wondering if, in your system, one can do whatever one wants. A friend of mine did *est*, and then just went crazy–had affairs, left her husband–and I think that's wrong.

JORDAN: So you're feeling very judgmental. We all judge others and ourselves. Unfortunately, not only are judgments not helpful, but we can't learn anything while we are judging. *Judgments about behavior are what block learning.* Another way to look at this would be with an intention to learn. You would then want to learn about the very good reasons she had for behaving as she did and about your judgmental reaction to her.

   As with all behavior, there are always important reasons behind someone's choice to have an affair. It may not have been in her best interest to make that choice. It may have been a protection. It may be that she went out and had affairs because she was addicted to sex, addicted to the affirmation that she got from sex. It may be that she was running away from intimacy and that was the way she did it. There are all kinds of reasons why a person would have affairs that are not healthful for them. *But to the person making the choice, they are important reasons and that choice probably appeared to be the best thing she could do at the time.*

There is always another choice. She could choose to learn about: her part in the situation; her fears that are being touched off; her beliefs; why the other person does what he does; whether he is open to explore that with you. There are a lot of things she could learn before she leaves the relationship. A person's first reaction is often "Well, I could leave the relationship or I could accept it." The option rarely considered is: "I could explore and learn a lot about this upsetting situation." She may eventually leave the relationship and this may be the most loving thing to do, but people usually leave prematurely before they learn anything about their own part in the relationship. They will usually go right into other relationships with different people, but with the same dynamics.

Since the woman you described is not here, would you like to explore what might be creating your judgmentalness?

(In the interaction that followed, this woman explored her pain over an infidelity in her past, her fears concerning her husband's love for her, and her desire to have control over other people's actions. She saw her judgments as a protection, a way taking the focus off her own painful feelings, and recognized the devastating effect these repressed emotions were having on her relationships.)

SHARING: How do you not take another person's behavior toward you personally?

MARGIE: Knowing that a protection is always a cry for help may help you respond in a loving way. People who feel good about themselves, sure that they are indeed

77

okay, do not react protectively. Protections always come from fears. When you judge your own protections, you're not being loving toward yourself. When you take another person's protection personally, you feel attacked and you can't be there for that person in a loving way. If you could see that the person is fearful and you were to respond from love, you would be soft, open and interested. You would not take that person's criticism, anger, coldness, shutdown, irritation, or insensitivity as an affront to you. Therefore, *you* would not be in pain and so rather than reacting defensively, you could reach out in real concern. You would feel forgiveness, in the truest sense of the word, from your Higher Self, not from your judgmental ego.

JORDAN: When Margie gets irritated with me, my first reaction has always been to tighten up and get defensive: "You're not going to do that to me, I'll give it right back to you!" If I didn't take her irritation personally, if I didn't feel like a bad boy, if I didn't feel wrong, then I could realize that she's hurting when she's irritated, and I would react in an entirely different way. I could speak to her and focus on her and be loving in the face of her unloving behavior. The reason I am not loving in the face of her unloving behavior is because I've seen it as an assault on me and then become protected. To see that the other person's protections are always a cry for help is a profound awareness and a profound truth. It can be very hard to see, but it's always true.

Now go to the next page and do the exercise.

EXERCISE 3B–FORMAT FOR FINDING THE LOVING BEHAVIOR

PART 1 – Taking personal responsibility for a conflict

1. When do you or did you feel like a victim?

    (Preferably pick a situation you're still in. If you can't think of one, then pick a past incident.)

2. How are you responsible for causing the initial incident?

3. Describe your own behavior in the conflict. How are you responsible for creating the interaction and the consequences.

PART 2 – Finding the loving response in a conflict

1. Using the situation you described in Part 1, think about what you could have done or could now do that would be loving and complete the following statement:

"A reaction that is loving and personally responsible is............ "

EXERCISE 4–CHECKLIST–SELF-LIMITING BELIEFS ABOUT RESPONSIBILITY

_____ 1. I can't make myself happy if someone around me is protecting him/herself.

_____ 2. I should never do anything that upsets or hurts another's feelings.

_____ 3. Others should never do anything that hurts or upsets me.

_____ 4. I don't need anybody.

_____ 5. Other people can make me happy.

_____ 6. Other people can make me unhappy.

_____ 7. I can't take care of myself.

_____ 8. I can't be alone. I'll die if I'm alone.

_____ 9. When I'm hurt, it's someone else's fault.

_____ 10. I shouldn't feel happy when people around me are unhappy.

_____ 11 I shouldn't do something that makes me happy if someone else is upset about it.

_____ 12. I can make someone else be open and loving.

_____ 13. I can get other people to stop their protected behavior.

_____ 14. It's up to me to make the people I care about happy.

_____ 15. When I'm unhappy it's someone else's fault.

_____ 16. When others around me are unhappy, it's my fault.

_____ 17. It's my responsibility to make sure that the people around me don't fail.

_____ 18. If I don't take responsibility for other people's happiness and unhappiness, I'm not a caring person.

_____ 19. I don't deserve to make myself happy. Therefore someone else has to take responsibility for telling me it's okay to do what makes me happy.

_____ 20. If I take responsibility for my own happiness, I'm being selfish.

_____ 21. It's selfish of me to be happy unless everyone around me is happy.

_____ 22. (For women) As a woman, it's my job to see that everyone is happy.

_____ 22. (For men) As a man, it's my job to make sure that the woman in my life is taken care of financially.

_____ 23. It's up to other people to make me feel good about myself by approving of me.

_____ 24. I'm not responsible for my feelings. Other people make me feel happy, sad, angry, frustrated, shut down or depressed.

_____ 25. I'm not responsible for my behavior. Other people make me yell, act crazy, get sick, laugh, cry, hit, throw things, leave, fail, act nice or act mean.

EXERCISE 4–CHECKLIST–SELF-LIMITING BELIEFS ABOUT RESPONSIBILITY (Cont'd)

___ 26. If I'm loving and I make myself happy, other person will take advantage of me.

___ 27. If I'm loving, the other person will never change and be the way I want him or her to be.

___ 28. If I'm loving and I take responsibility for my own happiness, I won't need a relationship.

___ 29. If I'm in a relationship, the happier and more loving I become, the further apart we will get because I won't need a relationship.

— 30. It's my parents' fault, or my partner's fault, or someone else's fault that:

___ I'm unloving.

___ I'm scared to be alone.

___ I don't believe relationships can work.

___ I'm so screwed up.

___ I can't change.

___ I can't take care of myself.

___ I'm in a job I hate.

___ I'm an alcoholic, drug addict, compulsive over-eater or workaholic.

— 31. Fill in your own.

___

___

___

___

EXERCISE 5–LEARNING FROM UNMET EXPECTATIONS

We all have expectations. They are those statements which often start with, "If you really loved me...." Many have said that, ideally, you should live without expectations, since this would keep us totally in the present moment. This is obviously unrealistic.

We suggest a more practical approach. Accept that you're going to have expectations, but when your expectations aren't met, know that you have two choices:

1. TO PROTECT BY BLAMING: When you blame others for making you unhappy when they don't meet your expectations, you are accusing them of being unloving. They will probably get defensive and begin trying to prove that they do care. Then you will have arguments over whether they care or not. Because of your belief, they'll never convince you, and everyone will wind up feeling uncared for and misunderstood.

2. TO BE LOVING BY TAKING PERSONAL RESPONSIBILITY: When you learn from your unhappiness, you can discover the following: whether your expectations do, in fact, have anything to do with caring about others; what you do to create and perpetuate your unhappiness; how to take responsibility for doing what you need to do to change your present unhappiness.

Any time you notice yourself being judgmental, look for the expectation that wasn't met and then look for the belief that underlies the expectation.

Think of a recent time when your expectations weren't met.

1. Describe the incident, your reaction to it, the other person's reaction to your behavior and the scenario that followed.

2. Rewrite the scenario with the intention to learn. (An important learning will be to discover whether what you have believed is caring fits the definition of loving behavior.)

3. Go to the other person with an intent to learn. (You will have the opportunity to learn about caring on a deeper level.)

EXERCISE 6–CHECKLIST–SELF-LIMITING BELIEFS ABOUT EXPECTATIONS

If you really loved me (cared about me) you would: OR...
If I were really important to you, you would:

___ 1. Never do anything that upsets me.
___ 2. Remember my birthday (or anniversary).
___ 3. Never be late.
___ 4. Call me when you're going to be late.
___ 5. Be turned on to me.
___ 6. Make love to me whenever I want to.
___ 7. Never want to do anything without me.
___ 8. Never walk away when I'm talking.
___ 9. Stop reading when I walk in the room.
___ 10. Watch TV with me.
___ 11. Always want to do what I want.
___ 12. Agree with me.
___ 13. Have the same interests I do.
___ 14. Lose weight or gain weight.
___ 15. Make more money.
___ 16. Spend less money.
___ 17. Keep the house clean.
___ 18. Do the dishes.
___ 19. Eat right.
___ 20. Take your vitamins.
___ 21. Dress the way I want you to.
___ 22. Be affectionate.
___ 23. Be affectionate in public.
___ 24. Put your clothes away.
___ 25. Share the responsibilities at home.
___ 26. Put the toilet seat down after you pee.
___ 27. Put the toilet seat up after you pee.
___ 28. Always have an orgasm.
___ 29. Enjoy all the kinds of foreplay and sexual activities that I enjoy.
___ 30. Not have an orgasm until I do.
___ 31. Wash your genitals before coming to bed.
___ 32. Make me happy.
___ 33. Never take vacations without me.
___ 34. Take care of me.
___ 35. Always have dinner ready.
___ 36. Always look nice.
___ 37. Read my mind.
___ 38. Anticipate my needs.
___ 39. Never let me oversleep.
___ 40. Never be attracted to anyone else.

EXERCISE 6–SELF-LIMITING BELIEFS ABOUT EXPECTATIONS
(Cont'd)

If you really loved me (cared about me) you would: OR...
If I were really important to you, you would:

___ 41. Never make love to anyone else.
___ 42. Make my needs more important than your own.
___ 43. Give in to me.
___ 44. Do things my way.
___ 45. Call me every day.
___ 46. Make up first.
___ 47. Never argue with me.
___ 48. Buy me expensive presents.
___ 49. Give me more money.
___ 50. Solve my problems for me.
___ 51. Do all the things that I don't like to do.
___ 52. Make me feel good about myself.
___ 53. Take care of me whenever I'm sick.
___ 54. Not have outside interests or hobbies.
___ 55. Always want to be with me.
___ 56. Stop drinking.
___ 57. Stop taking drugs.
___ 58. Come home earlier from work.
___ 59. Spend more time with the kids.
___ 60. Stop watching so much TV
___ 61. Go to bed the same time I do.
___ 62. Take a shower every day.
___ 63. Never lie to me.
___ 64. Never think of old lovers.
___ 65. Make my unhappiness go away.
___ 66. Stop being friends with old lovers.
___ 67. Stop being friends with people I don't like.
___ 68. Tear up old love letters.
___ 69. Be excited about the things that excite me.
___ 70. Be interested in my problems.
___ 71. Always want to be with me.
___ 72. Make everything right for me.
___ 73. Love my pets.
___ 74. Love my parents.
___ 75. Love my children, be good to my children.
___ 76. Get rid of your everything that is a reminder of your previous marriages.
___ 77. Be serious when I want to be serious.
___ 78. Be miserable when I'm miserable.
___ 79. Be happy when I'm happy.
___ 80. Be miserable when I'm away.

EXERCISE 6A–CHECKLIST–SELF-LIMITING BELIEFS ABOUT EXPECTATIONS FOR CHILDREN

If you really loved me you would:

___ 1. Never do anything that upsets me.
___ 2. Agree with me.
___ 3. Lose weight or gain weight.
___ 4. Go to college.
___ 5. Do your homework.
___ 6. Get good grades.
___ 7. Eat what I cook.
___ 8. Eat with the family.
___ 9. Finish everything on your plate.
___ 10. Keep your room clean.
___ 11. Do your chores.
___ 12. Eat right.
___ 13. Take your vitamins.
___ 14. Dress the way I want you to.
___ 15. Be affectionate.
___ 16. Put your clothes away.
___ 17. Give in to me.
___ 18. Do things my way.
___ 19. Call me when you're going to be late.
___ 20. Take a shower every day.
___ 21. Stop watching so much TV
___ 22. Stop taking drugs.
___ 23. Never argue with me.
___ 24. Talk to me about your problems.
___ 25. Never lie to me.
___ 26. Stop being friends with kids I don't like.
___ 27. Become a doctor (or a lawyer, etc.).
___ 28. Not leave dirty dishes around.
___ 29. Have good manners.
___ 30. Say "Please" and "Thank You."
___ 31. Be good in front of my friends.
___ 32. Appreciate the things I buy for you.
___ 33. Be the person I want to be.

EXERCISE 7–REVIEWING THE DAY FOR LOVING AND UNLOVING BEHAVIOR

This is an exercise designed to help you learn about loving behavior on a daily basis. You can do this out loud with a partner or just think about it before going to sleep at night. This is also a wonderful exercise to do with the entire family, perhaps at the dinner table.

1. Think of one or two unloving things you did during the day. Focus on how these behaviors were unloving toward yourself, how they didn't leave you feeling really good about yourself. In the midst of a conflict, did you try to control another person, or did you give in, shut down or became indifferent? Recapture how you felt about yourself. What would have been loving behavior? What fears and beliefs got in the way of your behaving in that way?

2. Now think of one or two loving things you did. Recapture how you felt when behaving that way. Allow yourself to drift into sleep with the images and feelings of being your Higher Self.

Do not expect your learnings will be easily accomplished. You are just beginning your journey down a very unusual road.

THE ROSE

Some say love, it is a river
That drowns the tender reed.
Some say love, it is a razor
That leaves your soul to bleed.

Some say love, it is a hunger
An endless aching need.
I say love, it is a flower
And you its only seed.

It's the heart afraid of breaking
That never learns to dance.
It's the dream afraid of waking
That never takes a chance.

It's the one who won't be taken
Who cannot seem to give,
And the soul afraid of dying
That never learns to live.

When the night has been too lonely
And the road has been too long;
When you think that love is only
For the lucky and strong

Just remember, in the winter,
Far beneath the bitter snow,
Lies the seed that with the sun's love
In the spring becomes the Rose.

–Amanda McBroom

CHAPTER

· 4 ·

FORMATS FOR LEARNING

The formats for learning in this chapter are designed to help you focus your learning. They will guide you into many different areas in which it is possible to learn, so that completing them in depth will give you a fuller picture of why things are the way they are in your life. This includes the critical area of *being open to learning about what gets in the way of your willingness to learn.*

These formats can be used individually or with a partner. Individually, you can either write out your answers or speak them into a tape recorder. Use whatever method is most helpful in bringing you to your own answers.

Doing these with another person will be an entirely different experience. Your partner can help you focus and perhaps go deeper than you can go alone. On the other hand, it is often very tempting for your partner to try to influence you. Or it may be easier for you to slip into focusing on the other person rather than yourself. See what works best for you and know that no matter what happens, you can learn from it.

The first format in this chapter is the most basic format for learning from a conflict and you will probably use it the most. It's especially useful because of the importance of continuing to increase your awareness of your protections.

All of the Self-Limiting Beliefs Checklists can be used with these formats. However, to help you focus your thinking, we are including in this chapter a summary of the most common self-limiting beliefs. You will find this page following the first format.

You can start using the formats right away even though many questions within the formats are the subject of subsequent chapters. As you do the exercises in those chapters, coming back and using these formats again and again will increase the depth of your learning.

Sharing from the workshop
after using the Basic Format for Learning

SHARING: I've done this workshop twice before and this is the first time that I've understood that the real key is challenging the beliefs. That's how I get rid of the old baggage. If I don't do that, I just don't achieve anything.

MARGIE: That's right. You can look at what you've been doing and what else you can do, and why none of this is working; but until you get down to the belief that is governing the fear which leads to the behavior and decide how to challenge that belief, nothing is really going to change.

SHARING: Let's say you want to challenge a belief, but you don't have the confidence to challenge it. How do you convince yourself or the world or somebody else that you really do want to challenge it and that you are capable of challenging it?

MARGIE: If you really want to challenge the belief, then you go ahead and challenge it no matter how frightened you are. Challenging a belief *is* frightening. There is no way around it. If you believe you have to get beyond your fear *before* you challenge beliefs, you will never challenge them. If you have beliefs that cause you to lack confidence, then you have to deal with those beliefs before you can move on. Sometimes we just have to act. You know, we are all really terrified that bad things are going to happen. You just have to tell yourself, "Okay, I'm willing to fail" or "I'm willing to lose" or "I'm willing to be laughed at or ridiculed" or whatever it is that you are afraid of. You have to be willing to have the worst thing happen. This the only way through the fear.

You are also dealing with your ego. We are all dealing with our egos. Your ego wants to prove that it's right. And so when you challenge your ego, you're trying to prevent your ego from sabotaging your efforts. You are always dealing with an ego that wants its own beliefs to rule.

But you also have a will. You decide. You can hear the voice of the ego, and you can hear the voice of the Higher Self. The voice of the ego is very loud and the voice of the Higher Self is very soft, but you can hear it if you want to. It is your choice which one you listen to. It is your decision.

When you decide to challenge your beliefs, that ego is going to come in powerfully: "What are you, nuts? How can you do this? You're going to DIE. You're going to lose everything." It's going to come in with all its beliefs and hit you over the head. It's your choice to listen to the old beliefs or to go ahead without them.

SHARING: So we are learning to silence the ego.

MARGIE: Yes, and the only way you can silence the ego is by challenging its beliefs. Once you see that the belief is false, then the ego can no longer hit you with it. You must thus quiet the ego and listen carefully to hear your Higher Self.

EXERCISE 8–BASIC FORMAT FOR LEARNING FROM A CONFLICT

1. What is the situation I am unhappy or upset about?

2. How am I protecting in this situation right now? (Detailed in Chapter 5)

3. What do I hope will happen as a result of my reacting in this way?

4a. Are my protections working to get me what I want?

4b. What is the actual result (the consequences), for my relationship and for myself of my reacting protectively? (Detailed in Chapter 6.)

5. What is my part in creating the situation? (Look at your part in the on going history of this conflict.) Describe the various ways you have been protecting yourself in the events leading up to this conflict. (Detailed in Chapter 6.) This may be the same protection as in #2, or a different protection or protections.

    (If you have difficulty answering this question, ask the person with whom you are in the conflict.)

6. What fears/beliefs (about protections, about my adequacy, and about expectations) are creating my protective behavior? (Detailed in Chapter 7.)

7. What in my past experiences created these fears/beliefs?

8. What would be the loving behavior? What would be the opposite of how I've been protecting? What would be the behavior that would bring me joy, support my growth, enhance my self-esteem and make me happy as well as support the other person's growth? Describe how the behavior looks. Be concrete. (Review Chapter 3.)

9. If I can't do that, what fears/beliefs are getting in the way of my behaving in a loving way? (Detailed in Chapter 7.)

10. Am I willing to challenge the accuracy of these fears/beliefs with loving behavior? If not, I have just made the choice to stay stuck with my unhappiness. To get unstuck, I must explore the beliefs and fears that have led to my unwillingness to test out the above beliefs:

    a) What purpose is being served by my hanging on to this belief?;

    b) What am I afraid would happen if I let go of this belief?

Once you have learned more about your protections and you really know your protections don't work, then you can shortcut this process by focusing more on questions 6, 8, 9 and 10. This format can be used until you wear it out.

THE MOST COMMON SELF-LIMITING BELIEFS

Beliefs about control:
- Attempting to control through creating guilt and fear in others using my anger, blame, judgements or cries of "poor-me" will eventually get me what I want in life.
- Attempting to control another person is justifiable if that person does something I feel is wrong.
- If I'm not in control, then I'll be controlled, because in a relationship, you're either one-up or one-down.
- I can get another person out of his or her protected behavior.

Beliefs about compliance:
- If I do things to make myself happy, I'm selfish. To be unselfish, I have to give myself up to make others happy.
- I have to give myself up to make the other person happy, or that person won't love me.
- Going along with what others want, even if it's not what I want, is a loving way to be.
- What I feel and want isn't important.
- I should never do anything that upsets or hurts another person's feelings.

Beliefs about resistance:
- Rebelling is a good way to establish one's independent identity.
- It's the controlling person's fault that I resist or rebel.
- If I don't rebel, I'll be controlled.

Beliefs about indifference:
- I can avoid problems by becoming indifferent.
- It's better to shut down and withdraw than reach out and risk rejection.

Beliefs about adequacy:
- I'm not good enough. Therefore, I have to:
    - control to get what I want.
    - give in to avoid rejection.
    - shut down to avoid the pain that I can't handle.
- I'm inadequate, unlovable, not good enough because...
- If I'm wrong about anything, it means I'm stupid or not okay and I'll be rejected.
- I can't handle pain, especially the pain of rejection.

Beliefs about expectations:
- If I were really important to you (or if you really loved me or cared about me) you would...

EXERCISE 9–FORMAT FOR CHALLENGING SELF-LIMITING BELIEFS

Challenging beliefs is a simple yet difficult process. It is the heart of the transformational process. You can use this process for every self-limiting belief you have.

1. Where did I get this belief? What were the circumstances in which I can first remember accepting this belief?

2. How does this belief affect my life right now? What are the situations in which this belief comes up?

3. What are the negative consequences of this belief?

4. What are the positive consequences of continuing this belief? (What are the payoffs? What am I getting? What am I avoiding?)

5. What is the behavior that would challenge this belief? (If I didn't believe this, if I began to call this belief a lie, how would I feel and behave?)

6. Am I willing to try out that new behavior? (If not, you need: more time, more information and/or more negative consequences.)

EXERCISE 10–EXPLORING BELIEFS ABOUT ISSUES OF RIGHT AND WRONG

When there is some issue that you want to learn about, you can use the next format. This includes any of the things you get upset about when you believe there is one right way to think, feel and act–being on time, clean, monogamous, honest, prudent with money, mature. The following is a list of possible conflict issues:

Sex–frequency, technique, initiation of
Money–control of, uptightness about, looseness with
Politics
Religion
In-laws–attitude toward, reactions to
Communications–amount of, clarity of
Commitments
Responsibilities
Holidays and gift giving
Criticalness
Manners–table manners, social etiquette
Television
Sports
Schoolwork–grades, homework
Children–how to raise, how many, when, whether to have any
Other relationships–sexual and non-sexual
Looks–grooming, weight, dress, neatness, cleanliness
Housekeeping–neatness, chores, who does what
Time–compulsive about being on time, always late
Time–how time is spent; amount of time spent together, at work, with others, doing hobbies
Vacations–how often, how spent
Work–differing attitudes, priority in life
Use of substances–alcohol, drugs, tobacco
Health–exercising (too much, too little), taking care of self physically
Food–what is healthy, amounts, who cooks, when to eat
Language–proper use; choice of words
Humor–lack of, being put down by
Affection–amount, how expressed
Pets–whose responsibility, whether to have
Feeling taken advantage of

Learning about these questions of right vs. wrong is an important part of your learning. The next format will take you not only into your beliefs, but also into your need to be in control. This need to be in control is a most basic issue for all of us.

EXERCISE 10—FORMAT FOR EXPLORING BELIEFS ABOUT ISSUES OF RIGHT AND WRONG

1. What do I believe is right or wrong and how is this belief being "violated?"

2. Why do I believe this way?

3. What purpose does it serve for me to hold on to this belief?

4. What am I afraid would happen if I let go of this belief?

5. Is this a God-given universal belief shared by everyone throughout the world? (If your answer is yes, you might do some research to see if it really is. If no, go on to the next question.)

6. Why is it so important to me to have my way on this issue?

7. How do I make others wrong when they don't believe as I do or do things my way?

8. What am I afraid would happen if I didn't make others wrong?

9. What do I hope will happen by making others wrong?

10. What happens when I attempt to impose my beliefs on others?

11. Why is it so important that others believe the same way I do?

12. Am I willing to test out the accuracy of my beliefs? If yes, how am I going to do that? If no, why not?

EXERCISE 11–LEARNING FROM YOUR FEELINGS

Most people have no idea what is causing their feelings. Protective feelings always come from beliefs. When you accept that, you take full charge and responsibility for your feelings. Protective feelings will never be changed by trying to change them. They will change when your beliefs change.

You don't choose to feel depressed, angry, or scared, but you have chosen the beliefs that create these feelings. You can avoid taking responsibility for your feelings by believing that others cause your feelings or that feelings just descend on you, and that you are powerless to do anything about it. Taking responsibility for your beliefs and feelings is one of the most loving things you can do.

Now, "taking responsibility for your feelings" doesn't mean blaming yourself, hating yourself, feeling guilty or beating yourself up for all the mistakes you've made. The idea is not to stop blaming somebody else only to turn all your judgments against yourself. The idea is to love others and love yourself–remembering that you have good reasons for your behavior, looking for and understanding the beliefs that create your behavior, accepting and forgiving, and then finding the new, more loving beliefs on which to base your new, more loving behavior. The last step of the cycle occurs when you finally test out the new beliefs and behaviors to see how they work.

One of the hardest truths to accept is that it is not possible to be emotionally hurt by somebody. Since feelings are a result of beliefs, if you are feeling emotionally hurt, *it is because of your beliefs, not someone else's actions.*

Not taking another's behavior personally is the goal. Once you have corrected your own erroneous beliefs, your behavior will look and feel entirely different to other people. You will see and feel things from a new perspective. You can then behave with caring toward ourselves and others. You will see and care about the pain others are creating for themselves, and if they choose not to change their unloving behavior, then it would be loving to yourself to get away from their unlovingness.

EXERCISE 11–FORMAT FOR LEARNING FROM YOUR FEELINGS

1. How am I feeling? Write down as many feelings as you are aware of:

Angry	Threatened	Hurt	Guilty
Irritated	Insecure	Disappointed	Unworthy
Frustrated	Jealous	Depressed/"Dead"	Wrong
Inadequate	Scared	Blaming-victimized	Unlovable
Uptight	Resentful	Anxious	Bored

2a. Where in my body do I feel these?

2b. How deeply am I allowing myself to feel these feelings?

3.* What are the judgments I have about feeling this way? Do I feel wrong, guilty, inadequate, unlovable, weak, stupid?

4.* What do I fear would happen if I just allowed myself to reach the depths of these feelings?

5. What events from my past are connected to these feelings? What circumstances from the past do these feelings remind me of?

6. Am I interpreting another person's behavior as an assault on me?

7.* How am I hoping another person will respond? Do I want another person to do something? What am I hoping another person will do about my feelings?

8. If my feelings are blaming–resentment, anger, wronged, hurt, "poor me", righteous–what vulnerable feelings are being covered up?

   sad, scared, alone, disconnected, unsure, confused

9. What are the beliefs that are creating both my vulnerable feelings and my blaming feelings?

10. What happens in my relationship(s) when I protect against my vulnerable feelings?

11. What would be the loving behavior towards myself that would lead to my feeling better?

12. What fears/beliefs are getting in the way of my loving behavior?

*The answers to Questions 3, 4, and 7 relate to self-limiting beliefs and can be explored separately for deeper learning.

EXERCISE 12–FORMAT FOR LEARNING FROM YOUR REACTION TO AN EMOTIONAL VIOLATION

When you have been emotionally violated in any way, your reaction to that violation is going to determine how you feel about yourself. Your buttons get pushed whenever another person criticizes, belittles you, is angry with you, or demonstrates any other abusive behavior. Whenever you take another's behavior personally, it's because it taps into your own self-doubt. That's your opportunity to learn about your self-doubt and begin to clear it out. This is the format you can use.

1. What do I feel when I am violated emotionally (criticized, made the butt of a joke or sarcasm, ignored, discounted, teased, made wrong, belittled)?

    hurt, angry, abused, used, uncared for, indignant

2. What happens in my body? I feel:

    a knot in my stomach; queasy; weak; deadened; tense; pain in various parts of my body; faint; nauseous

3. How do I react when I feel I have been emotionally violated?

    attack back; wimp out; smile; withdraw; get embarrassed; try to be different to please the other person; go along with the "humor"; inform the other that my feelings are hurt and I'm not going to take it anymore; blame myself; make nice.

4. What is my part in this emotional violation? What set me up to be vulnerable to it?

    What expectations or "needs" of mine weren't met?

    Why am I taking this personally?

    Do my hurt feelings serve some purpose? What are they protecting me from?

5. What happens to the relationship as a consequence of my reactions?

6. What is the loving thing to do–the behavior that will enhance my self-esteem?

7. What fears/beliefs are getting in the way of my loving behavior?

EXERCISE 13–QUESTIONS TO ASK WHEN WANTING TO KNOW ANOTHER

As with everything else, the results of using this format will depend on your intention. If your intention is not to learn, then you can use the words written here to manipulate another. The words you use with another person are really unimportant, since your *intent* is what determines the outcome of any interaction.

When you're really wanting to learn about another and you say gently and lovingly, "You know, what you've done is upsetting me, but I know you must have some important reasons for having done it. Would you tell me what they are?" The other person will very probably perceive that you really want to know. But if you say accusingly and harshly, very judgmentally and with no warmth or caring "You know, what you've done is really upsetting me, and I know you must have some important reasons for having done it. I'd like to know what they are," there is no intent to learn on your part. The other person will immediately know that you really only want to accuse. The words don't mean anything. Our intention comes through in the tone of voice and in the energy that we put out. We put the words on paper to help you, but you can't rely on the words. It's the energy that will be responded to. Everyone instantly picks up, on a conscious or unconscious level, whether another person's energy is open, as opposed to being upset, shut down or judgmental.

* What you've done is upsetting to me, but I know you must have some important reasons for having done it. Would you tell me what they are?

(or)

* You seem upset (or angry, distant, defensive, etc.) You must have some important reasons for feeling that way. Would you tell me what it is?

(or)

* You seem upset (or angry, distant, defensive, etc.) Have I done something that hurt you?

(or)

* Is there something that I'm doing that's upsetting to you?

Then you can move to the format for exploration for yourself and/or your partner.

SYMPTOMS OF INNER PEACE
By Saskia Davis

Be on the lookout for symptoms of inner peace. The hearts of a great many have already been exposed to inner peace and it is possible that people everywhere could come down with it in epidemic proportions. This could pose a serious threat to what has, up to now, been a fairly stable condition of conflict in the world.

Some signs and symptoms of inner peace:

- *A tendency to think and act spontaneously rather than on fears based on past experiences.*
- *An unmistakable ability to enjoy each moment.*
- *A loss of interest in judging other people.*
- *A loss of interest in interpreting the actions of others.*
- *A loss of interest in conflict.*
- *A loss of the ability to worry. (This is a very serious symptom.)*
- *Frequent, overwhelming episodes of appreciation.*
- *Contented feelings of connectedness with others and nature.*
- *An increasing tendency to let things happen rather than make them happen.*
- *An increased susceptibility to the love extended by others as well as the uncontrollable urge to extend it.*

WARNING!

If you have some or all of the above symptoms, please be advised that your condition of inner peace may be so far advanced as to not be curable. If you are exposed to anyone exhibiting any of these symptoms, remain exposed only at your own risk.

CHAPTER

· 5 ·

MOVING OUT OF PROTECTION

Sometimes when you are protected, you may know it. You may feel it in your body and you may say "I'd like to learn," but somehow the tension, the anger, the upset, and the judgment are there and it is really hard to move from a protected place into the intention to learn. In this chapter, you will learn some techniques for moving out of the intention to protect and into the openness to learning. These exercises may produce some learning, but that's not their primary purpose. The learning that leads to the profound changes that occur when beliefs are questioned and changed will come from the formats in the previous chapter.

EXERCISE 14–THE LEARNING LETTER

When you are upset and feeling like a victim, sometimes you can't just say, "Okay, I'll let it go now. I want to learn." You may need to find a way to let it out. To open, you may need to begin with your upset feelings, your angry, blaming, victim feelings and release them.

A very effective way to do this is to write a Learning Letter. The Learning Letter helps you move through your anger and other blaming feelings into your fear, your hopes, and then into your love. Once you reach love, you will be in the intention to learn. The purpose of the letter, then, is not so much to help you learn, but to help you move out of the intention to protect and into the intention to learn.

For the most part, when people get angry they just blame another person and that's where they get stuck. That's why just expressing your anger when your intention is not to learn will keep

103

you stuck in a cycle of anger. But you don't have to stay stuck in your angry or "poor me" victim feelings. If your intention in being angry is to *get past* the angry feelings, to get past any blaming feelings and get into an open state, then it may be a very important part of your process to express your anger or to express any of your blaming feelings. That's what this letter gives you a chance to do–to really go with your blame, to be in your ego, to be a nasty little kid, to be a victim, or whatever it is. If your intention is to get through those feelings, then when you do get through them to the other side, you'll be open. You will find your softness there, and you may find your tears, too.

Even in the middle of an argument, you can stop and say "I don't want to do this. I'm going to write." You can go off by yourself and use the Learning Letter. Write as long as it takes you to write out your feelings. Keep writing until you feel a shift inside of you. The shift is moving from the consciousness of being protected to the consciousness of love, the openness of the intent to learn. The shift is definite and you will feel it.

You may choose to share the letter with the person to whom you're writing, but its primary use will be to help you to get through your own protected feelings. Knowing that no one will see this is very freeing. You don't have to worry about hurting someone else's feelings, incriminating yourself, "bad" language, messy writing, misspelling, or grammar. The idea, as we've said, is for you to have a way to let yourself go and really get into it...and through it.

If you do choose to share your letter with the person to whom you've written, be clear with your intent. Is your intent to get the other person to: understand you, feel guilty, feel afraid? Do you want to change the other person? Is your intent for him to learn? If so, your intent is manipulative, and you will probably get a defensive response.

It's always rather amazing how much feeling this process can touch off in people. Writing is a powerfully cathartic process that takes many people deep into themselves. The Learning Letter can be used for guidance any time you're upset. It is a very powerful tool.

To practice this exercise, think of a conflict in your life that is unresolved, frustrating, or that brings up feelings of being a victim. Find something you have wanted from another person for a long time and haven't gotten. This can be with a mate, ex-mate, parent (alive or dead), child, boss, employee, friend, sister, brother, God, yourself, any person in your life with whom you have a problem, with whom you're feeling angry or upset. Come up with a juicy issue. If you have trouble coming up with an issue, refer to the list of possible conflict issues on Page 95.

Look over the Learning Letter Format. The sentence completions are there to help you tap into your feelings. You can use any of them or all of them. In Part 1, express all your angry, blaming and victim feelings onto the paper. Keep writing until you move into the consciousness of openness. You will know you have reached this place when your body relaxes. Then move on to Part 2.

EXERCISE 14–FORMAT FOR THE LEARNING LETTER

Each letter has two parts:

      I)   All the blaming feelings that come from your protections;

     II)   All the non blaming feelings that lie under your protections.

Use the following lead-in phrases to help touch off what you are feeling and wanting:

I)   BLAMING FEELINGS – These are the feelings that make your partner responsible for your condition.

    A)   Express your anger, irritation, resentment, and criticism.

> I (hate it) (don't like it) when you...
> I'm (fed up with) (tired of) your...
> You're just a...
> You should/shouldn't...
> It's your fault that...
> How could you...
> The problem with you is...
> I can't stand...
> If it weren't for you...
> You make me crazy when you...

    B)   Express your hurt, disappointment, unhappiness, jealousy and pain – your "poor me" feelings.

> I feel hurt when you...
> You make me feel...
> I feel disappointed when you...
> I feel jealous when you...
> I feel rejected when you...
> If it weren't for you...
> If only you...
> It's devastating to me when you...
> I feel so unhappy when you...

Continue writing your blaming feelings until you feel yourself shift into the intention to learn. Then go on to the next page.

EXERCISE 14–FORMAT FOR THE LEARNING LETTER (Cont'd)

II)   NON BLAMING FEELINGS - These are the feelings that arise when you stop blaming others and take responsibility for the fear and sadness that result from your own choices–your part of the difficulty. When expressing non blaming feelings, the tension will drain from your body and you'll feel soft, open and vulnerable. Write all you can about your vulnerable feelings, your fears, sadness and insecurity. Then write about your hopes and your loving feelings. Remember, there is nothing for you to fix. It's okay to feel what you feel without trying to solve a problem.

A)   FEAR - Express your fear, anxiety, and insecurity.
I feel scared when I...
I feel scared when you...
I feel tense and anxious when you...
I feel scared that you don't care about me when you...
I'm afraid to let you know how I really feel because...
I feel scared that we...

B)   SADNESS - Express your sadness over your own choices.
I'm sorry that I...
I feel (bad) (awful) when I...
I feel sad that I...

C)   HOPES - Express what you want, your dreams and wishes, not your demands.
I often dream that we could...
Sometimes I fantasize that...
I wish I felt...
I wish you felt...
I wish that...
What I really want is...

D)   LOVE - Express your love, caring, and understanding.
I love you because...
I love it when you...
What I love most about you is...
Thank you for...
I understand that...
I appreciate you for..

Once you've written your letter, move on to a format for exploration.

EXERCISE 15–PASSIVE LISTENING

This exercise can be used when you are in a conflict and both you and the other person are protected and want to move into a intent to learn, or when you want to move out of your protections but the other person is stuck. The exercise may seem very simple. However, its profoundness may surprise you.

All you're going to do is just listen while your partner talks for five minutes. In the second part, you'll have a chance to talk for five minutes and have your partner listen to you. It may be hard just to listen, but it will probably feel wonderful to be listened to. That is something that we usually don't get, so it's a special opportunity to talk about anything that's on your mind.

If your partner is not the person with whom you have the conflict, imagine that your partner is that person and say the things you've been holding back.

Suppose that you're angry with one of your parents. Tell the person who is listening, "You're going to be my mom and I'm going to talk to you as if you're my mom." Your partner just listens as if he or she is your mom.

The listener needs to be present and listen with the heart, not the mind. Really be there and hear the other person. Eye contact is very important. You will have to resist the tendency to defend and explain, even though you may disagree. Remember that silence does not mean agreement. You are just going to listen to another person's feelings, giving him a chance to express feelings to you.

Before you do the exercise, take a few minutes to read the following piece, entitled "Listen." You may come to understand why being listened to is so rare, and why it feels so good when it happens.

LISTEN

When I ask you to listen to me and you start giving advice,
You have not done what I asked.

When I ask you to listen to me and you begin to tell me why I
*   shouldn't feel that way,*
You are trampling on my feelings.

When I ask you to listen to me and you feel you have to do something
*   to solve my problem,*
You have failed me, strange as that may seem.

Listen! All I asked was that you listen, not to talk or do
*   –just hear me.*

Advice is cheap: twenty-five cents will get you both Dear Abby and
*   Billy Graham in the same newspaper.*

And I can do for myself; I'm not helpless. Maybe discouraged and
*   faltering, but not helpless.*

When you do something for me that I can and need to do
for myself,
You contribute to my fear and weakness.

But when you accept as a simple fact that I do feel what I feel, no
*   matter how irrational, it may seem easier for me to quit trying to*
*   convince you and I can get about the business of understanding*
*   what's behind this seemingly irrational feeling.*

And when that's clear, the answers are obvious and I don't need
*   advice. Feelings make sense and are respectable when we*
*   understand what's behind them.*

Perhaps why prayer works, sometimes, for some people, is because
*   God is mute and doesn't give advice or try to fix things.*

Those who care enough to just listen, communicate that they have
*   faith that you can work things out for yourself.*

So, please listen and just hear me. And, if you want to talk, wait a
*   minute for your turn; and I'll listen to you.*

In the process of expressing your feelings and talking about the situation, you may find that if given the space just to talk and get your feelings out, you may come up with some solutions and awarenesses that you didn't even know about before you started. That is often the case, and is one of the powerful gifts that come from just being listened to. The answer to all your problems, the answer to all you want to know is inside of you. Nobody else has the answers for you. You just need to find a way to get to your own knowing. When you are protected and you don't know how to get out of your protections, you can say, "Okay, let's just have a ten minute exercise. I'll talk for five minutes, then you talk for five minutes." Just listen to each other, don't be planning what you'll say when it's finally your turn. REALLY LISTEN.

During your time to talk, you can say anything you want. If you're angry, be angry. If you're blaming, be blaming. If you're a victim, be a victim. It's your arena to be where you are emotionally at that moment and be heard. You don't have to be open, loving, or in your Higher Self here. You have an opportunity to say anything you want and have the other person hear it.

You can talk to one person or five people, if you feel like it. This is your time. Couples don't have to talk about the same issue; each of you can choose anything you want. If you run out of things to say and the other person wants to ask questions, you're probably moving into the intention to learn. This is a listening exercise, not a process for learning. It is releasing–saying things, explaining, defending, whatever it is that comes up for you when you are in a protected place. This is a way of getting to the point of where you open to exploration.

A variation on this exercise would be to set aside twenty minutes and after each person has spoken, each gets another five minutes to speak and listen again. That's how we do it in our workshop.

Now is your chance to do the exercise.

EXERCISE 16–ACTIVE LISTENING

Active listening differs from passive listening in that the listener feeds back to the person who is talking what he hears the speaker saying and feeling. This is obviously more difficult than passive listening since the listener has not only to be in tune with the speaker, but has to give verbal feedback as well. It's impossible to actively listen when you are protected. When you are not protected, but another person is, active listening may help that person to open. When you know that you are protected and you want to move into openness, you can ask someone to actively listen to you. We will give you just a brief description of active listening. There are more detailed explanations available in *Parent Effectiveness Training* by Dr. Thomas Gordon and *Your Child's Self-Esteem* by Dorothy Briggs.

With active listening, you let the other person know that you understand his feelings by putting the *feelings* that are under his words into your own words and feeding them back to the other person with empathy. Being empathic, i.e, feeling into the other's feelings, feeling *with* the other, is the most important aspect of active listening. You encourage the other to express all his feelings, both positive and negative. When active listening, you don't ask the other person *why* he feels a certain way–you just accept his feelings. Your sentences might start off with "Sounds like you're feeling..." or "I'm hearing you say that..."

It may be easier to understand what active listening is by describing what it is not. It is not:

asking leading questions	looking away, being
giving advice	distracted or bored
disagreeing	showing the error in
explaining	the other's thinking
discounting	placating
changing the subject	making helpful suggestions
denying the other's	joking
feelings	exaggerating

denying your own feelings or behavior	giving examples of other's behavior
getting angry	comparing
judging	defending
telling own stories, feelings	interrogating
	excusing
telling child how he/she feels	analyzing
	parroting the words
problem solving	adding your interpretation
lecturing	adding your feelings or ideas
giving lip service	
condescending	

In other words, any time you respond protectively, you are not actively listening. When you get defensive, try to problem-solve, or attempt to talk others out of their feelings, you miss a wonderful opportunity to learn more about them and they miss an important opportunity to learn about themselves.

When you listen to other's feelings, some of your feelings may be triggered: your fears of inadequacy; possible problems in your marriage; fears relating to the job you're doing as a parent; your ability to handle a particular situation; facing your own feelings that may be similar to the speaker's feelings.

When you find that you can't actively listen to another, you can explore and learn about what's getting in your way, what fears and beliefs are being tapped into. Are you afraid the speaker's emotions will touch off your own? Do you believe the speaker is not capable of resolving his problems? Are you afraid the speaker can't handle the painful feelings that might come up? Do you believe it will take too much time?

Active listening gives the other person the feeling of being understood. Enough cannot be said about the importance of feeling understood. It's one of the best feelings in the world, like a breath of fresh air, or a sigh of relief that accompanies "Somebody cares enough to want to understand me."

Feeling understood is an important part of feeling cared

about. Not feeling understood almost always keeps protections in place. Once we feel understood, protections often dissolve and we become open to the deeper awareness that comes through exploration.

EXERCISE 16–FORMAT FOR ACTIVE LISTENING

1. Ask someone who is close to you to tell you something he is upset about *related to someone other than you.* Actively listen to him.

2. Ask the same person or someone else to tell you *something he's upset about.* Actively listen to him.

    You will probably find it easier to actively listen when what the other person is upset about has nothing to do with you. You can learn a lot about what gets in the way of your ability to actively listen.

3. Ask someone to actively listen to you. You may need to explain to him what active listening is. During the time he is listening to you, you may need to tell him when he's not actively listening.

Remember, this is a tool to move into an *openness* to learn; the learning occurs through your exploration.

EXERCISE 17–FORMAT FOR BREAKING A POWER STRUGGLE AND LEARNING FROM IT

Power struggles are an inevitable consequence of protections. A power struggle occurs when you try to get something from somebody and it doesn't work. He doesn't give it to you. So, you try to get it in another way or the same way. You try harder and he resists. Power struggles exist in almost all relationships. They can be centered around talking–" I want to talk and he doesn't" , "I want to make love and she doesn't" ; they can be centered around being on time, cleaning up your room (that's how parents and children get into power struggles very early), doing homework, just about anything.

The real issue at the root of any power struggle is "I'm not going to be controlled by you." You try to get something from somebody else, you try to *make* something happen. The other person resists because he doesn't want to be controlled by you. You get stuck in an unending circle. You throw up your hands and say, "It seems like such a simple thing. What's the big deal?" Someone's integrity is at stake. That is the big deal. It has nothing to do with being on time or cleaning your room or anything like that.

Breaking a power struggle requires letting go, accompanied by the intention to learn.

This exercise is designed to help you learn about power struggles, your part in perpetuating them, and how to end an argument and open to learning. Permanently breaking a power struggle requires the in-depth learning to be found in the Basic Format for Learning in a Conflict (Chapter 4). The exercise must be done with another person, but not necessarily the person with whom you're in the power struggle. Because it is in three parts, and a little more complicated than most of the others, first read through the entire exercise and then do one part at a time.

In this exercise, you will experience three different interactions: a fight (both people protected); one person changing his intention; and then both people opening to learning–all in 5 minutes.

Each of you chooses an ongoing issue that you have been upset about, something you have wanted from another person and have been trying to get for a while. Choose a juicy issue, something that's really important to you.

Once you have found your issue, sum up to yourself what you want in one sentence. Examples: "I want you to talk with me." "I need you to make love with me more often." "I want you to be on time." "I want you to do your homework." "I want you to stop taking drugs."

Now decide, for the first round, who will be the Controller and who will be the Resister. After you go through the four parts of the exercise, you will switch positions so you each get a chance to be a Controller and a Resister. Read through the entire exercise before you attempt to do it.

EXERCISE 17–FORMAT FOR BREAKING A POWER STRUGGLE AND LEARNING FROM IT

PART 1:   Protect/Protect

1.   Controller: You're going to try to get your way, to get the other person to give in to your wishes. You're going to use every verbal device you have ever used and you might even try some new ones. You're going to try to win through creating fear and guilt in the other person.

   Resister: Put your complaint aside for now and come back to it after Part 4 when you switch roles. You *will not* give in to the demands of the Controller and will take a passive but defiant position. You will not be controlled.

2.   Stand across from each other, assume your combative postures and hurl your statements back and forth, e.g: Controller: "I want you to be on time." Resister: "Don't you tell me what to do" or simply "No way!!!" You will go back and forth and as the tension mounts, so will your energy.

3.   Before you begin, close your eyes for a few moments and get yourselves ready for the ensuing battle.

   Controller: Feel that hard, tight place inside you that wants to be right and win and that feels the other is wrong.

   Resister: Feel that tight place inside you that will not be run over. Nobody is going to tell you what to do!

4.   Take two minutes for this part of the exercise.

PART 2:   Protect/Open

Resister: Consciously shift your intention to an openness to learning. Respond with statements that come sincerely from this openness, "I don't want to argue, I just want to learn with you." "I don't want to argue, I just want to love you." It might be easier the first few times with your eyes closed to get into the feeling before opening your eyes. Take twenty to thirty seconds to shift your intention. Close your eyes and take some deep breaths. Feel how much you hate to fight, how much you want to be close and loving, how much it hurts to fight.

116

Controller: Continue to stay with your desire to win. Stay with your power statements. Stay with your belief that if you just try harder of find new and creative ways to control, you will eventually get your way.

Take two minutes for this part of the exercise.

PART 3: Open/Open

1. Both partners sit down. Controller, consciously shift your intention to the openness of learning. Both partners feel how much it hurts to argue, how much you want to be loving and be happy, how tired you are of fighting.

2. Take each others' hands and go back and forth with a loving and learning statement, "I want to be close to you, talk to you, be friends with you, explore with you." Do this for one minute with your eyes closed.

3. Open your eyes and look into each others eyes while continuing to say your loving and learning words. Feel your own and the other's love and caring. Do this for one minute (or longer, if you want!).

PART 4: Discussion

Discuss the experience for about five minutes to learn as much as you can from it.

1. Controller: Be aware of how it felt in your body when you needed to win and were afraid you would lose. Notice how difficult it was to continue to feel powerfully angry when you got a loving response. How often are you in that situation? How does it feel to soften and open?

2. Resister: How did it feel to be in the resistant position? How often and in what situations are you in that position? How did it feel to soften and open?

PARTS 5-8:

Reverse roles and do the exercise again.

You can use the idea of shifting your intention any time you are in an argument to break a power struggle and open the door to learning.

If you're in an argument and the other person is not available to learn with you, you can still say, "I don't want to argue, I want to learn" and go and learn. Learn by yourself. You don't need the other person there to do your learning. You can learn all by yourself or with a third person. If you believe that you have to have your mate (or whoever you're in conflict with) there in order to learn, then you are making yourself into a victim, and you are going to be after that person, pulling on that person. Anytime you want to learn, you can go learn.

If your partner is not open to learning, then leave your partner for the time being and go do your own learning. You can write, call a friend or do any number of things for yourself. Remember, *battering up against somebody else who isn't open is not loving to yourself or to that other person.*

(Now you can go back and do the exercise.)

EXERCISE 17A–CHECK LIST–SELF-LIMITING BELIEFS ABOUT BEING RIGHT/WRONG

Often, limiting beliefs about right and wrong are at the heart of a power struggle. Who is right and who is wrong? In this situation, the intention to learn will bring you face to face with your fears of being wrong. Take a minute to see which of these beliefs you hold.

____ 1. If I'm wrong about something, others will think less of me, or reject me.

____ 2. If I'm right, others will love me.

____ 3. If I make a mistake, it means I'm stupid, or not okay, and I'll be rejected.

____ 4. If I'm right, I'm smart, or okay

____ 5. If I'm wrong, I lose.

____ 6. If I'm right, I win.

____ 7. It's possible to get love, or get what I want, by being right.

____ 8. It's better to be right than to be loving.

____ 9. I must make others see that I am right to make them respect me.

____ 10. I have to make myself wrong to get myself to change.

SUMMARY: WAYS TO DISSOLVE PROTECTIONS

1. Write a Learning Letter

2. Consciously shift your intent: "I don't want to argue,
    I just want to love you."

3. Passive Listen

4. Actively Listen

5. If you are too angry to write or listen:

    a. Express your anger physically using a pillow or a rolled-
    up towel and hitting a chair or bed while screaming out your anger.
    You can also go in a closet or in your car and scream.

    b. Do some physical activity, like walking around the block.

    c. Recall an intimate time and the loving feelings you had
    for another person.

    d. Change your physical environment – go to a movie, go
    for a drive.

    e. Listen to *You Are Your Higher Self* tape or other guided
    visualization or progressive relaxation tapes.

    f. Listen to relaxing music.

    g. Cry.

    h. Play with a pet.

    i. Call a friend and have him/her listen to your anger.

6. MOST IMPORTANT OF ALL–Take advantage of your new openness to get
    to the *origin* of your protective behavior. Dissolving your protections
    without going further with your learning is an exercise in futility. The
    ideas above can be used to patch things up. Feelings can be dissolved
    but unless the beliefs that have caused them are cleared up, you will
    always be at the mercy of your ego feelings.

MAKING A DIFFERENCE

Until one is committed there is hesitancy, the chance to draw back, always ineffectiveness. Concerning all acts of initiative (and creation) there is one elementary truth, the ignorance of which kills countless ideas and splendid plans; that the moment one definitely commits oneself, then Providence moves too.

All sorts of things occur to help one that would never otherwise have occurred. A whole stream of events issues from the decision, raising in one's favor all manner of unforeseen incidents and meetings and material assistance, which no person could have dreamt would have come their way.

I have learned a deep respect for one of Goethe's couplets...

**"What ever you can do, or dream you can, begin it.
Boldness has genius, power and magic in it."**

—*W. H. Murray*

CHAPTER

·6·

PROTECTIONS & CONSEQUENCES

PROTECTIONS

Controlling, giving in, rebelling, and becoming indifferent are reactions to fear. Protections are neither right nor wrong, good nor bad in themselves. Either they are working to bring you joyful feelings or they are causing you unhappiness. Rather than looking at right/wrong, you can look at what they create. The focus of this chapter is to help you understand more about your reactions to conflict and what those reactions create.

Housekeeping, lateness, sexuality, money, in-laws and child raising are just a few of the hundreds of issues that are the source of conflicts. A more detailed list of conflict issues is on page 95. The issue may be your unhappiness over the lack of connection or communication in your life. How you approach another with your unhappiness is another level.

The two levels of communication in a conflict are:

1. The actual issue of the conflict
                    and
2. How you are reacting to the conflict

Picture a garden. There are weeds coming up and the soil is poor. You cut the weeds, but the soil is lousy and nothing else will grow in it, so the weeds keep coming back. You keep cutting them down and they keep coming back. You cut them down, they come back. The weeds are the ISSUES between you, like communication or money or whatever you argue over. And you keep arguing over them and resolving them and then they come up again, the same issue over and over again. You never directly address HOW you are dealing with the issue.

Once you learn how to learn, you can resolve any issue. It doesn't matter what the issue is. Until you learn how to learn, no resolution is possible. For this reason we will ask you to forget the specific issues for now and concentrate on your protections. (The Formats for Learning in Chapter 4 are to understand how to learn from your individual conflicts.) Before you can learn from your issues, however, you must resolve the blocks to your being open to learn and those start with your protections.

There are two basic categories of conflicts and protections:

1.   Conflict: Another person does something you don't like and/or think is wrong.

   Protection: You attempt to get that person to change her behavior or thinking, i.e., you try to CONTROL or become INDIFFERENT.

   and

2.   Conflict: You do something that another person doesn't like and/or thinks is wrong and she attempts to get you to change your behavior or thinking.

   Protection: You become COMPLIANT/REBELLIOUS/ INDIFFERENT or CONTROLLING (trying to get the other person not to be controlling).

Everyone reacts protectively in both of the above situations most of the time. Therefore, you will find yourself in all of the following categories although some may be a more consistent part of your personality than others.

Any time you find yourself feeling defensive, blaming, self-righteous, shut-down, or victimized, you are protected, closed, not open to learning. In fact, *anything other than an intention to learn is protective.*

You protect out of fear that you're going to lose something or somebody else. As you learn about the ways you protect, it's important for you not to say "Oh my God! I'm such an awful person, how could I do this!" You're afraid, that's how. We all protect when we're afraid. What you need to do is become aware of the ways you protect yourself when you're upset.

We have said this before and will say it many times: there are good reasons why you protect. We're sure you've recognized many ways you attempt to control, and there isn't anybody in the world who doesn't try to have control over others. You try to control when you're afraid that if you don't, you're going to be controlled and something bad is going to happen. Obviously, there are a lot of negative consequences connected to protections, but you aren't bad or wrong for trying to control those around you. You need to acknowledge that you try to control before you can ever make any changes. It's really hard for all of us to look at how much we control. Many people fill out the Controlling Position Checklist (Page 132) and think, "What else is there? Of course I do that. I do all those things. I can't even imagine another way of being." Almost all human interactions are about control and manipulation; they are certainly not about learning. It may be hard to face. And it is harder to face when you judge yourself.

The Controlling Position–Your Attempts to Change Another

We all want others to change and often it would even be best for others. Wanting change is not the problem, *attempting to get others to change is what creates the difficulties.*

This section is designed to help you become more aware of how you attempt to have control over, to manipulate, others. You believe that if only they would change their behavior, you would be happy and, of course, so would they. You become controlling when you're upset with someone else's behavior: someone is doing something you don't like, you're not getting your way, you think they're wrong or you're afraid for them in some way.

You believe you are right and others are wrong and therefore you have the right to impose your beliefs on them. "If I'm right, then I have the right to control." We're not saying there's no right or wrong, but just to notice that when your intent is to prove you're right, you're not wanting to learn.

The many good reasons you have for attempting to be in control all have to do with your fears. You try to control when you feel powerless and know of no other way to feel powerful and not to lose.

It's important to check out your beliefs about how people change. Most people believe that change comes about by imposing negative consequences, in other words, by creating fear. There's no doubt that people sometimes respond to fear, but there is always a great negative cost to both the person attempting to impose change and the person on the other end of these attempts. Take a good hard look at your own reactions when people attempt to get you to change and the reactions of others around you when you attempt to get them to change. Notice how effective you are, the results of your efforts. Is it worth it?

Meaningful change with no negative consequences happens through the intention to learn. It's in the process of getting rid of our false beliefs and feeling better about ourselves that the most satisfying changes take place. *Change that results from caring and not from fear leaves everyone feeling more satisfied.*

One of the reasons it's so hard to acknowledge controlling behavior, is because it's behavior that puts other people in pain. Attempts to change others give them the message that their behavior is wrong, and it never feels good or loving to be made wrong. Remember, even though your behavior inflicts pain on others, that is not usually your primary intent. Your primary intent is to protect yourself. We don't say this to allow you to justify any behavior or make it right, only to reduce the self-judgments which are never helpful.

You may not know right now on a conscious level all the ways you attempt to get others to change. The following is a brief description of some of the typical ways people attempt to have control over others.

(More detailed descriptions of controlling behaviors can be found in *Do I Have to Give Up Me to Be Loved By You?* pages 165-172 and in *If You Really Loved Me...* pages 57-80.)

Crying–Crying can be a protection when you are crying as a victim. "Poor me. Look what you're doing to me. You're making me feel miserable. You better feel guilty." Now, the person who is crying usually is not consciously manipulating. She does really feel bad and is really crying, but she feels like the victim and hopes that the other person will feel guilty and change his behavior.

Not all crying is protective. There are two kinds of tears: the tears that come from the intent to protect–"Poor me, look what you are doing to me;" and the tears that come from the intent to learn–"Pain is a teacher and I am willing to feel my pain in order to learn."

Telling your feelings–Crying is very closely related to telling your feelings. The key as always is intent. What is the intent of telling your feelings? Is your intent to learn from your feelings, to learn about yourself, why you're feeling this way, what the lesson is here? Or is your intention to get other person to change or to justify your feelings? You probably aren't consciously aware of your intent and have been taught, if you've been exposed to psychology at all, that it is good to tell your feelings. However, as with all interactions, the words are less important than the intent. Consider whether you tell other people your feelings in order to scare them or make them feel guilty or sorry, and thus alter their behavior toward you. Is your intent to learn or is your intent to get others to learn so that they'll change?

Anger–The message is, "You're bad, you're wrong, I'm going to be upset with you until you do it my way. The hope of anger is to frighten the other person into doing things your way."

Pouting–We pout in hopes that other people will feel guilty. And if they do, then they'll change.

Silence–Silence can be golden, but it can also be filled with tension. The Cold Shoulder. The Look. The Evil Eye. The message is "You've done something that's upset me and this is what you're going to get every time you upset me, and you're going to get the cold shoulder until you repent!"

Offering solutions, problem solving–"Why don't you do it this way? If only you do it this way, you'll be fine." You're rational and calm, but the intent is still the same–to get the other person to change. When you're trying to solve problems, your intent is not to learn, it's to *remain in control*, to protect yourself by solving the problem.

Interrogation–Where were you, who were you with? You interrogate when you're afraid. You're waiting for the other person to say something you can pounce on. Through interrogation, you gather information you can use in some way or to feel safe.

Being a "nice guy"–You act nice to get something, to get someone to be nice to you. (Women can be "nice guys" too.)

Threats–Physical harm, withholding money, leaving the relationship, any kind of punishment. You only threaten people at their weak or vulnerable points. For example, you only threaten physical harm if they are smaller or weaker than you. Parents who hit their children will often say "Well I can't help myself. I get upset and it just happens." If the child was 6'8" and weighed 280 pounds, they would probably make a different decision. The same thing is true with money. You don't threaten to withhold money from a wife who works and earns as much or more money than you do. You use that threat with non-working women and children.

Explaining–"I'll explain to you how wrong you are, show you the error in your ways, show you the light, the right way." When you are lecturing or explaining, your intent is not to learn anything about yourself or the other person. That is the key. Your intent is to get her to learn so that she'll change her ways.

Convincing, or selling yourself–When you say "But don't you remember the time when..." and "Look at how I've changed," you're promoting how good you've been rather than opening to learning what is going on in this moment.

Denial–Denial is a form of control because when you deny, you attempt to determine the other person's reality: "That never happened!" "I don't remember that!"

Criticism–Criticism can take the disguise of "This is for your own good" or a sarcastic remark or making "fun" of another. The message is the same: "You are wrong."

EXERCISE 18–HOW DO YOU LOOK AND SOUND WHEN YOU'RE ATTEMPTING TO CONTROL?

Think about relationships you have now or have had in your life. Remember times when you were upset because you weren't getting what you needed or wanted and you tried to get others to change their behavior, times when you criticized them, yelled at them, withdrew in anger, threatened them. Did you want to make them feel guilty or scared? When you are upset, how, specifically, do you try to control people? Do you yell or criticize? Do you walk away? Are you judgmental, irritated? Do you lecture and explain? Do you tell your feelings? Stop for a while and think about what you do.

Get a picture in your mind of how you look when you're upset with another. Who do you remind yourself of when you try to control someone else? Is the way you control others similar to the way another family member used to control you? Do you treat people the same way you were treated as a child? Stop for a while and let the connections happen.

If you're experiencing discomfort with yourself now, it's because as you admit to your controlling ways you're judging yourself: "I shouldn't do things like that! I'm horrible!" It would be helpful if you could remember that your controlling behavior is your protection. You can't learn when you're judging. You're not bad or wrong, just scared and unaware. We all control at times. We had to learn these behaviors as children to survive, and now it's time to learn about them, not judge them. So let yourself know that you have very good reasons for your controlling behavior - your deep fears of being controlled by others, or of losing their love and being rejected by them. We all want control over how others behave and react to us.

Now go on to the next page and do the following format.

EXERCISE 18–FORMAT FOR HOW YOU LOOK AND SOUND WHEN YOU'RE ATTEMPTING TO CONTROL

1.   Write down as many different incidents as you can recall in which you attempted to control other people.

2.   Again picture yourself in your controlling behaviors. Try to see yourself as others see you when you're in a controlling posture. Our image of ourselves probably comes from all those pictures we've seen of ourselves when we're smiling and open. Most of us never see how we look when we're closed, hard, defensive, angry, pinched in, withholding, critical. We are very aware of how *others* look but remain blissfully ignorant of ourselves.

3a.   See if you can act out your controlling behavior in front of a mirror. Exaggerate it.

Or

3b.   Draw a picture of yourself.

Or

3c.   Have others who have been on the other end of your controlling behavior (spouse, children, employees) show you how they see you. (This is a very courageous thing to do!)

4.   Write about how it feels to realize what a controlling person you are.

EXERCISE 18A–CHECKLIST–THE WAYS YOU ATTEMPT TO CONTROL OTHERS

1)   How do I try to control in my relationships?

___ Yell	___ Get angry	___ Use sarcasm
___ Criticize	___ Argue	___ Raise my eyebrows
___ Say "Tsk,tsk"	___ Lecture	___ Whine
___ Shake my head	___ Explain	___ Shrug my shoulders
___ Get annoyed/irritated	___ Become self-righteous	___ Make comparisons
___ Accuse	___ Blame	___ Throw things
___ Pout	___ Complain	___ Interrupt
___ Become ill	___ Convince	___ Tell my feelings
___ Be sneaky/deceptive	___ Justify	___ Withdraw angrily
___ Lie/withhold truth	___ Judge	___ Act like a know-it-all
___ Therapize	___ Flatter or give	___ Interpret
___ Be a "Nice guy"	false compliments	___ Teach
___ Be a "Nice gal"	___ Interrogate	___ Push the other
___ Give gifts with strings	___ Deny	into therapy
attached	___ Talk others out	I use:
___ Sulk	of their feelings	___ The silent treatment
___ Take responsibility	___ Ask leading	___ Disapproving looks
for others	questions	___ Disapproving sighs
___ Moralize	___ Bribery	___ Blaming tears
___ Bitch/nag	___ Scowl	___ "Poor me" tears
___ Analyze	___ Explore the	___ Temper tantrums
___ Be short/curt	other person	___ Put-downs
___ Be indispensable	___ Spank	___ A superior attitude
___ Give advice	___ Change the subject	___ Half truths

(Add any other ways you control in your relationship):

Threats of:
___ Financial withdrawal   ___ Abandonment
___ Emotional withdrawal   ___ Illness
___ Sexual withdrawal   ___ Violence
___ Exposure to others   ___ Suicide

2)   How do I feel when I am trying to control?

___ Anxious	___ Scared	___ Tense, uptight
___ Unloving	___ Unlovable	___ Deadened, shut down
___ Empty	___ Lonely	___ Hurt
___ Righteous	___ One-up	___ "Poor me" victim
___ Martyred	___ One-down	___ Bad
___ Sad	___ Frustrated	___ Upset
___ Wrong	___ Hardened	___ Sullen

EXERCISE 18B–CHECK OFF LIMITING BELIEFS ABOUT CONTROL

___ 1. I can eventually get others to do what I want them to do.

___ 2. The only way I'll get what I want from others is to *make* them do what I want.

___ 3. If I gave up attempting to control others I'd lose, I'd never get what I need.

___ 4. When I'm right, it's okay to try to make others conform to what I believe.

___ 5. There are no negative consequences of attempting to control.

___ 6. My attempts to control people will eventually earn me their love and appreciation.

___ 7. I can have control over others' liking me, loving me, caring about me, respecting me.

___ 8. I can have control over whether or not people reject me.

___ 9. My attempts to control my partner won't have any negative effect on his/her desiring to make love with me.

___ 10. I can have control over someone's desiring me sexually.

___ 11. My attempts to control someone can be camouflaged so that they don't know they are being manipulated, and there are no negative consequences.

___ 12. I am currently aware of all the ways I attempt to control others, so there is nothing for me to learn about.

___ 13. Attempting to control and being in control work to get me what I want. It makes me happy.

___ 14. Since attempting to control others is a sign of caring, they should appreciate it.

___ 15. Controlling behavior is so deeply ingrained that it's impossible to change it.

___ 16. I don't ever attempt to control people in my life.

___ 17. Attempting to have control over others is wrong.

___ 18. I'm bad if I try to control others.

EXERCISE 18B–LIMITING BELIEFS ABOUT CONTROL (Cont'd)

___ 19. Attempting to control through creating guilt and fear in others with my anger, blame or "poor me" will eventually get me what I want in life.

___ 20. My anger is something that just happens. I have no control over it.

___ 21. When I'm angry, people should know I'm really hurt.

___ 22. My anger doesn't hurt others.

___ 23. To attempt to control when I know I'm right is a loving way to be.

___ 24. Attempting to control people works to teach them lessons you want them to learn.

___ 25. Controlling people is a good way to teach them personal responsibility.

___ 26. Being controlling will protect me from being in pain.

___ 27. It feels good to dump my anger on another person.

___ 28. Attempting to control another person is justified when that person does something I feel is wrong.

___ 29. Being angry is a loving thing to do if it's for the other person's own good.

___ 30. I have to stay in control because I don't have a Higher Self to rely on. Everyone else does, but I don't. (Or, there is no such thing as a Higher Self.)

___ 31. I can win in a power struggle.

___ 32. If I don't let people know I'm angry they won't know how I feel, and they won't pay attention to what I want or consider how I feel.

___ 33. The only way people will take me seriously is if I'm unhappy, depressed or angry.

___ 34. Judging or criticizing people will get them to change. Once they see I'm right they'll change.

___ 35. By controlling others, I can make their behavior predictable.

___ 36. If I'm not in control, then I'll be controlled.

The Compliant/Rebellious/Indifferent Position - *When another attempts to control you.*

When another person attempts to have control over you, and you attempt to get them to stop, *you are trying to have control over their trying to have control over you.* In this kind of conflict, there are other protective behaviors we all manifest. This section will help you become more aware of them. Note that these protections are not directly controlling; they are your protections in reaction to someone trying to change or control *you.*

EXERCISE 19–LOOKING AT COMPLIANCE/EMOTIONAL CARETAKING

Compliant behavior results from your fear of hurting others' feelings or your fear of them hurting yours. For example, you might make love when you don't feel like it out of fear that the your partner will be angry with you and yell or withdraw, or out of a belief that your partner will suffer from your decision and you feel responsible for his feelings. As another example, you might go along with what your boss wants even though you feel it's unfair.

Compliant behavior results from fear, obligation or guilt. Behavior is not compliant when it comes from desire and caring. For example, a person may not feel sexual but may feel loving and want to make love as an expression of that feeling.

At times, we all give in and go along with what the other person wants. This obviously doesn't fit the definition of loving behavior. It doesn't nurture your own emotional and spiritual growth, it is not a personally responsible thing to do for yourself, and it doesn't nurture the emotional and spiritual growth of the other person. People who comply a lot believe it's their job to be emotional caretakers. These are the people who say "I can't hurt his feelings. I'm a bad person if I hurt his feelings, so I'll just go along. It's okay."

Many people, grow up being caretakers, believing that they have to put their needs aside for other people. They believe that if other people are unhappy or upset, it's their fault, and so it's better for everyone if they give themselves up. We have all received a stiff dose of this belief.

Taking responsibility for someone else's feelings doesn't give either person the opportunity to deal with the truth. It creates a system in which both people are stuck. Caretaking is dishonest. It indicates that you're afraid, and when you're doing something out of fear, you are not doing what you really want.

EXERCISE 19A–HOW DO YOU RATIONALIZE COMPLIANCE?

When you are giving yourself up, what are you saying in your head? The following are some examples of how people rationalize compliance:

- "Oh, it doesn't really matter. It's not important anyway."

- "It's not a big deal."

- "It's best for the family."

- "I don't want to hurt him, because he can't take it."

- "It won't be important tomorrow."

- "It's easier than getting into an argument." (Peace at any price. It's easier than telling the truth and seeing what happens.)

- "If I don't comply, I could lose him, so I better go along."

- "What I really want I can't have, so I might as well go along."

- "If I say what I want, I'll cause an argument." (Do you know what caused the argument in reality? He reacted protectively and you reacted protectively. That's what caused the argument. It wasn't what you said in the first place.)

- "It's what's expected of me."

- "It's okay to lose me, but I can't lose my partner."

- "It's the right thing."

Think about how in your life you are being a "good boy" or "good girl"...Do you hold back from saying how you feel, because you don't want to make people angry at you? Do you often do what someone wants, because you don't want him to disapprove of you or pull away? Do you give up what you want to please others? Stop for a while and feel.

Can you remember a time when you didn't want to do something your partner, parent, child, boss, or friend suggested, but went along with it anyway, because you were afraid not to? Came home before you really wanted to? Spent money on something you didn't want to or not spend money on something you really wanted? Let someone make love to you when you really didn't want to? Just take a breath, and remember how it feels inside... When you feel like saying no, and you don't, do you feel weak and frightened? Angry at yourself or at the other person? How does it feel inside when you let someone else control you?

1. Think of and list all the things that you tell yourself when you comply.

2. Think of situations when you typically comply. Describe how you look and what you feel about yourself.

3. How do you feel about the other person?

4. What happens between you and another person when you comply?

EXERCISE 19B–CHECKLIST–THE COMPLIANT POSITION

1) What are the ways I comply when others attempt to control me, or I want to avoid their anger?

＿I don't ask for what I want.
＿I don't say anything.
＿I say something is okay with me when it's really not okay
＿I don't express my own opinion.
＿I agree with whatever others say.
＿I give up my own dreams and goals.

EXERCISE 19B–CHECKLIST–THE COMPLIANT POSITION
(Cont'd)

___I go along with whatever people want me to do.

___I give up what I want to do.

___I don't stand up for myself.

___I give away my power.

___I give up knowing what I want so I don't have to fear not getting it.

___I postpone talking about problems.

___I don't make waves.

___I do things to please others and get confused about what I want.

___I acquiesce.

___I take the "easy" way out.

___I censor what I say about what I want and how I feel.

___I rescue others while ignoring my own needs.

___I second guess or anticipate what others want.

___I down play my needs.

___I give in for now, thinking I won't have to next time.

___I tell myself that what I want isn't important.

___I tell myself that giving in is no big deal.

___I tell myself that what I want is wrong.

___I tell myself it's not worth the battle.

___I tell myself I don't deserve it.

___I tell myself it's worth it to get the other to shut up.

___I'll give in now because I'll take a stand later.

___I tell myself it's better to give in than hurt someone else's feelings.

2)   How do I feel when I protect in this way?

___Anxious	___Scared	___Tense, uptight
___Unloving	___Unlovable	___Deadened, shut down
___Empty	___Lonely	___Hurt
___Righteous	___One-up	___"Poor me" victim
___Bad	___One-down	___Martyred
___Sad	___Frustrated	___Upset
___Wrong	___Angry	___Sullen
___Hardened	___Weak	

EXERCISE 19C–CHECKLIST–SELF-LIMITING BELIEFS ABOUT COMPLIANCE

____ 1. Going along with what another person wants will insure that she or he will love me.

____ 2. I can avoid problems by giving myself up.

____ 3. Giving myself up doesn't lower my self-esteem.

____ 4. Going along with what others want, even if it's not what I want, is a loving way to be.

____ 5. There are no negative consequences to behaving out of fear, obligation or guilt.

____ 6. Love requires doing things that you really don't want to do.

____ 7. Complying is a good way to resolve conflicts.

____ 8. I have to comply or lose love. I can't be myself and be loved.

____ 9. A nice person complies in order to make another person happy.

____ 10. Complying will protect me from pain.

____ 11. Complying is more loving than any of the other protections.

____ 12. A good person never walks away from someone who needs him or her.

____ 13. If I do things to make myself happy, I'm selfish. To be unselfish, I have to give myself up to make others happy.

____ 14. If I say "no" to someone who wants something from me (sex, money, time, affection, attention, etc.), I'm selfish, and I feel guilty and afraid of rejection.

____ 15. Complying with others is a sign of strength. When I go along with what others want I am in my Higher Self.

____ 16. I don't have the right to feel what I feel and want what I want.

____ 17. If I do what I want to make myself happy, bad things will happen to the people I love.

____ 18. If I do what I want to make myself happy, I will end up alone.

EXERCISE 20–LOOKING AT RESISTANCE/REBELLION

This behavior occurs when you don't give in and you don't attempt to change another; instead you resist by rebelling passively or actively. Somebody wants you to do something and you don't want to do it, but you're not willing to just say "no." You may be aware of that part of you that tightens and says silently, "Don't you tell me what to do!" It's the part of you that may even rebel against your own commands to yourself. For example, you want to diet and you go to the refrigerator and see something you'd like but shouldn't eat. One part of you says, "Don't you eat that!" and the resistant/rebellious part snatches the forbidden food, saying, "Don't you tell me what to do!" It's the part that often passively rebels by not doing things well or doing them with a lack of enthusiasm. It's the part that often "forgets" to complete a task or is incompetent. See if you can tune into that part of you.

It's when you:

- say yes and then don't do it;
- say yes and resent it;
- say yes with no commitment;
- procrastinate;
- make others feel guilty for asking;
- end up saying "I forgot";
- think that there is a better way to do it;
- change it in someway to make it your own;
- do it, but do it badly.

Very often, people who tend to be really heavily controlling people also tend to be very resistant/rebellious people, because they're afraid of being dominated.

Think about your relationships. Remember a time someone wanted you to do something, and you rebelled or withdrew. You refused or said you weren't in the mood, or didn't like the idea...How were you really feeling inside? Is it possible that you wanted to go along, but were afraid of looking weak? Did you feel angry at the other people for telling you what to do and stubborn about not giving in? How did the other person react? Did he feel unloved? Did he feel rejected? Did he feel frustrated? Take a minute to close your eyes and remember the hurt.

Remember another time when someone wanted something from you...and inside you felt a voice saying, "Don't give in...don't do what he wants, or he'll control you forever..." How does it make you feel about yourself when you're resistant/rebellious? Stop and feel.

Now go to the next page and fill out the checklist.

EXERCISE 20A–CHECKLIST–THE RESISTANT/REBELLIOUS POSITION

1)   What are the ways I resist when someone attempts to control me?

       ___ I say I'll do what s/he wants and then I don't do it.
       ___ I do the opposite of what s/he wants.
       ___ I explain, defend, or get mad about why I shouldn't do it.
       ___ I get critical and make the other person wrong for asking.
       ___ I say I'll do it and then do something other than what the person wants.
       ___ I say I'll do it and then forget, or fail to show up.
       ___ I procrastinate.
       ___ I act helpless or incompetent.
       ___ I get apathetic - no enthusiasm.
       ___ I get sick.
       ___ I give to pets or friends what my partner wants.
       ___ I misunderstand, or am unable to understand.
       ___ I do it, but only half-way.
       ___ I do it wrong on purpose.
       ___ I find some way to sabotage the situation.
       ___ I pretend not to hear.
       ___ I'm disinterested.
       ___ I'm not open to learning.
       ___ I won't make a commitment.

2)   How do I feel when I protect in this way?

___ Anxious	___ Scared	___ Tense, uptight
___ Unloving	___ Unlovable	___ Deadened, shut down
___ Empty	___ Lonely	___ Hurt
___ Righteous	___ One-up	___ "Poor me" victim
___ Bad	___ One-down	___ Martyred
___ Sad	___ Frustrated	___ Upset
___ Wrong	___ Angry	___ Sullen
___ Hardened	___ Weak	

3)   What happens between me and another person when I resist/rebel?

EXERCISE 20B–CHECKLIST–LIMITING BELIEFS ABOUT RESISTANCE/REBELLION

___ 1. Rebelling is a good way to establish one's independent identity.

___ 2. My only choices when another person is attempting to control me are either to comply or rebel.

___ 3. There are no negative consequences to resisting or rebelling.

___ 4. I really am being my own person when I rebel.

___ 5. It's the controlling person's fault that I resist or rebel.

___ 6. Resisting and rebelling are automatic responses that just happen. I can't do anything about it.

___ 7. Rebelling and resisting will eventually work to get the other person off my back.

___ 8. My self-esteem is not lowered when I resist and rebel.

___ 9. To resist and rebel when I know I'm right is a loving way to be.

___ 10. Rebelling will protect me from pain.

___ 11. My rebelling doesn't hurt anyone.

___ 12. I can avoid being controlled by resisting and rebelling.

___ 13. When I don't want to do what others want me to do, they will not stop pressuring me unless I rebel.

___ 14. Rebelling is the only way to establish what I want. Otherwise, no one will hear me.

___ 15. Rebelling is the only way to get people's attention.

___ 16. If I didn't resist and rebel I would be controlled or swallowed up.

EXERCISE 21–LOOKING AT RESISTANCE/INDIFFERENCE

You may resist by becoming indifferent when you are afraid of domination. You don't want to give the other person the upper hand and you don't want to give yourself up.

Indifference doesn't involve trying to change others, doesn't engage others, but merely allows you to disappear emotionally and physically. Almost anything can be used to shut down and avoid facing difficult feelings, check out emotionally, vacate: drugs, work, sleep, reading, illness, TV, alcohol, food, sports, meditation. *Anything* can be used to shut yourself off to your own pain or to shut someone else out of you life. None of the things we use to shut down are inherently protective; it depends on your intention. If your intention in watching TV is to relax a little, that's one thing, but watching TV can also convey the message, "You can't get to me and this is the way I'm going to block you out." Look at the ways you spend time and see how much of it is done to avoid something else. For example, when you find yourself standing in front of the refrigerator looking for something to eat when you're not hungry, what would you have to confront if you *didn't* eat anything?

1. How do you shut the other person out and say "You can't affect me?"

    I shut down or ignore the person with:

___ Work	___ TV	___ Reading
___ Drugs	___ Alcohol	___ Sports
___ Hobbies	___ Children	___ Friends
___ Illness	___ Food	___ Sleep
___ Meditation	___ Story telling	___ Fantasizing
___ Spending money	___ Ruminating	___ Spacing out
___ Sex		

    ___ Fill in other ways you shut another out:

    (When you need these behaviors to feel good or relieve pain, you become obsessed with them, like an addiction.)

2. How do you feel about yourself when you become indifferent and/or avoid others? (Make a list.)

3. How do other people react to these behaviors?

4. How do their reactions leave you feeling?

EXERCISE 21A–CHECKLIST–SELF-LIMITING BELIEFS ABOUT INDIFFERENCE

____ 1. I can shut down and still enjoy life.

____ 2. I can shut down and still have intimacy.

____ 3. Indifference will protect me from feeling pain.

____ 4. My indifference doesn't hurt anyone. It it not unloving.

____ 5. I can avoid problems by becoming indifferent.

____ 6. I can avoid being controlled by becoming indifferent.

____ 7. Becoming indifferent is more loving than any of the other protections.

____ 8. Being indifferent does not lower my self-esteem.

____ 9. If I become indifferent, the problem will take care of itself.

____ 10. It's better to be shut down and withdraw than reach out and risk rejection.

CONSEQUENCES OF PROTECTIONS

When you decide to be protected, there are certain things that inexorably follow that decision. It probably doesn't feel as though you *decide*, because protections happen instantaneously. On some level, however, you are always making decisions about how you are going to behave, whether you are going to go with your ego or with your Higher Self. You always have that choice within you. It is your Will that makes that choice. If you insist that you don't have choice, that everything just "happens" to you, then you're off the hook; you don't have to be responsible for the conditions that you create. Most people think, "I am in pain because:

-   he won't talk to me;
-   he doesn't open up with me;
-   she doesn't want to connect with me;
-   she gets angry with me;
-   he doesn't work as hard as I want him to;
-   I don't have a partner and I'm alone;
-   the only way I can be happy is if I'm connected with somebody else."

Can you see the "victimness" of all the above thoughts?

Connecting your behavior to the negative consequences it produces is one of the most powerful motivations to bring about change. This means acknowledging the consequences of your decision to be protected: the consequences to you personally, to how you feel about yourself; and the consequences to your relationships.

Here are some of the seriously painful experiences that protections actually cause:

-   Feeling deadened when you shut down and become indifferent.
-   Feeling bad about yourself when you give in, injure others

146

or resist and rebel.

- Alienation from others as well as from yourself.
- Losing touch with your true nature and settling into either a lifeless existence or the pursuit of happiness by outward or material means that never give you the true joy that is possible in life.
- Your relationships become unsatisfying and again you either settle for much less than what makes you truly happy, or you make fleeting connections that give you temporary happiness and glimpses of what's possible, but you are left disappointed and unfulfilled.

You may feel your pain intensely or you may be just barely aware of the dull ache that comes from feeling disconnected and unfulfilled. Few people connect their pain directly to their own choices to protect themselves.

The most important thing to look at in terms of negative consequences is how you end up feeling about yourself. Is your self-esteem being raised or is it being lowered by your behavior?

The following are a few of the responses that came from workshop participants when we asked them to share the consequences of their protections. (Comments from Jordan and Margaret are in parentheses.)

My body is bent out of shape. It doesn't feel good, it hurts. I feel tense, tight, sick.

I feel needy and helpless.

I don't like the person I become. I feel bad right now when I even think about it.

I feel hateful. Everyone goes away. I end up feeling alone, alienated from other people and myself.

I lose my peace, my centeredness.

I feel deadness. (You feel deadened because you're not connecting with yourself. You are protected from yourself.)

I have to do a lot of managing. Life is hard.

I'm uncreative, tight and tense and everything is hard.

Confused and immobilized. I lose touch with my own knowing. I can't find my Higher Self when I'm in this tense, protected situation, so how can I know what I want when I'm like this?

I feel scared, worthless, depressed. (Depression, a consequence of protections, is present in our country on a vast scale. Look at the amount of drugs people take for depression. We say "I'm depressed because of something out there" rather than "I'm protecting myself and depression is the consequence.")

I feel confused. I look inside and nothing is there. It's empty. I don't know what I want or what I feel. (You cannot know what you want and feel coming from the ego. You can only know from the Higher Self, and you have to be willing to feel your pain in order to know that.)

Your automatic reaction in a conflict is guaranteed to be unloving and is the worst reaction. Skiing provides a good analogy for confronting our protections. When there is a steep place, a mogul or an ice field, the typical reaction to the fear is to tense up and hold your breath. You may or may not get down that slope without falling, but if you clutch onto your fear and tension the process of getting down is going to be hard work. It's an effort and you don't look or feel very good. What do you need to do to get down that slope with ease and grace, with the connected flowing motion of the expert skier? You need to breathe out and open. Open! Instead of your normal reaction, which is to tense up, you need to do exactly the opposite to stay centered, to flow.

The same thing is true in conflict. The first thing you do, your defensiveness, sets off a chain reaction which creates almost every difficulty in your life. The reaction which is most difficult–and most rare–is to stay open, to say, "What is my lesson here? What is this conflict telling me? Let's explore this. Let's learn. What is my fear?"

When you believe you can't handle difficult situations, you protect to avoid your present pain and your feared future pain. The paradox is that your protections bring about the pain. You're stuck. You are on a treadmill having to deal with the same problems over and over again. We all get the same lessons over and over again until we learn what the lesson has to teach us.

When you're having a particularly difficult time with someone in your life–mate, child, boss, friend–instead of trying to change him or figure him out, you can shift the focus to yourself. Ask yourself, "What is that person in my life to teach me? What do I need to learn?" There is an exercise to help you do this on page 208.

EXERCISE 22–THE SCENARIO OF YOUR PROTECTIONS AND THEIR CONSEQUENCES

This exercise can be done in three ways. You can write the scenario, say it into a tape recorder, or play-act both parts. Play-acting offers some great benefits: if you can really get into doing your partner's physical postures and behaviors, you will get a deeper understanding of how your partner feels and possibly of what s/he thinks, too. You may also begin to see some humor in the situation, strange as it may sound!

1. Pick an on going conflict you're having and make up a script detailing the interaction. Start with the conflict. (e.g., You want to make love and your partner isn't in the mood. If you're having trouble coming up with a conflict, go over the list of conflict issues on page 95.) Describe or act out your behavior and then your partner's reaction and your reaction to your partner's reaction. Be sure to include physical reactions, too. Do you avoid looking at each other? Do you cave in or go red in the face?

2. See if you can write/act what you're feeling with each response and what your partner is feeling. You can probably recreate the words exactly as they have occurred and will occur in the future. We usually know exactly what our behavior will be and what the results will be, but we keep doing the same things hoping that "This time it will be different; I'll get what I want; I'll win."

3. If you've tried variations on the same theme, write/act them. Do as many as you can until you know that your protections will always produce the same negative results. As long as you have hope that your protections will work, you will continue them.

4. To hasten the awareness that they will never work, intensify whatever you've been doing. After all, if you believe what you're doing will work, doesn't it make sense that more of it should work even better and faster?

EXERCISE 23–THE CONSEQUENCES OF YOUR PROTECTIONS

Think about a relationship you have in your life now–a relationship with a mate, a child, a parent, a friend, a boss, an employee. Remember a time when you tried to control that person with your anger, irritation, silence, criticism, blame, lectures, explanations, threats, tears, or any other of the ways you control. Notice the details of the situation; Where were you? Who else was around? What triggered it? How did he react? Did the other person cry, get angry back, get very quiet? Did he do what you wanted him to do? Did he resist and rebel against you?

How were you feeling inside when you behaved in these ways? What happens in your body, your stomach, your throat, your head? How do you feel about yourself when you are upset with someone and you try to control him? Do you ever feel embarrassed afterward? Do you ever feel hopeless or helpless?..... How does it make you feel to know that people you care about are scared of you? How does it make you feel to know that people you love are afraid to upset you? Does this make you feel powerful or does it make you feel depressed? Does it make you feel lovable or unlovable? Close your eyes and answer these questions honestly.

Now take a deep breath and let all those thoughts go. Remember a time in a present relationship when someone wanted you to do something and you complied or withdrew or rebelled. Choose only one and remember the incident in as much detail as possible. Where was it? Who was there? What was the issue? Stop and remember.

Take a breath and remember how you felt inside when you complied, withdrew or rebelled. Did you feel weak, frightened, tense, anxious, angry at yourself or at the other person? How do you feel inside when you either go along with what the other person wants or when you resist and withdraw, rather than being your own person and deciding what you want for yourself? Do you feel weak and unlovable? Feel what that feels like in your body. Stop and give yourself time to feel....

And now think about what happens between you and that

151

person that you care about. What is the outcome of complying or rebelling or withdrawing? Do you feel loving towards the other person? Do you feel loved? Even if you avoid conflict by complying, do you end up feeling loved and loving? When you rebel or withdraw–how does the other person react? Does he get angry? Does he withdraw? How does he feel inside? Does he feel unloved...rejected...frustrated?

Feel within you the many consequences of your protections and write about how you're feeling and what you're learning.

EXERCISE 23A–CHECKLIST–NEGATIVE CONSEQUENCES OF PROTECTIONS

STEP 1. Find the lists (A., B., C. and/or D.) of negative consequences that apply to the relationships you are in and check the ones that apply. Feel free to add your own.

STEP 2. On List E, the Negative Consequences to Yourself, check the ones that apply. Feel free to add your own.

A. Negative Consequences with A Partner or Past Partner
___ Our sex is infrequent and/or boring, no passion or love.
___ Our relationship is boring routine, with little excitement or intensity.
___ There is a feeling of distance between us.
___ My partner feels insecure about my love.
___ I feel unloved and/or insecure about my partner's love.
___ I feel unloving.
___ There is a lack of satisfying communication.
___ I like myself better when I am not around my partner.
___ My partner and I don't have much fun together.
___ I feel freer when my partner is not around.
___ My partner is lifeless, nothing seems important or exciting.
___ I feel resistant, rebellious, resentful a lot of the time.
___ My partner is often resistant, rebellious, resentful
___ I often lie or don't tell things to my partner.
___ My partner often lies or doesn't tell me things.
___ I often feel guilty around my partner.
___ My partner seems to act out of obligation.
___ I feel manipulated.

EXERCISE 23A–CHECKLIST–NEGATIVE CONSEQUENCES OF PROTECTIONS (Cont'd)

___ We're in a power struggle, each wanting only to win.
___ I feel on guard around my partner.
___ I don't feel valued for my accomplishments.
___ I don't share my partner's enthusiasms.
___ My partner doesn't share my enthusiasms.
___ Our conflicts are not reaching satisfying resolutions.
___ I feel jealous or envious.

B. Negative Consequences with A Child
___ We have constant power struggles.
___ I feel a lack of caring toward my child.
___ My child doesn't care about me.
___ My child is often angry and/or irritable with me.
___ I often feel angry or irritable with my child.
___ My child is often resistant, defiant, rebellious.
___ We have frequent hassles over things like chores, homework, tidiness.
___ My child has low self-esteem.
___ My child is doing poorly in school.
___ My child is often fearful, lacks confidence.
___ My child is often rejected by peers
___ My child is self-abusive.
___ My child is abusive or with other people and/or things.
___ There is an emotional distance between me and my child.
___ I feel inadequate as a parent.

C. Negative Consequences with Your Parent
___ We get into power struggles.
___ I feel controlled by my parent.
___ I feel the weight of obligations to my parent.
___ I feel emotionally shut down or dead around my parent.
___ I can't talk to my parent.
___ I feel rejected by my parent.
___ I feel inadequate in my parent's eyes.
___ I feel angry or irritated with my parent.
___ I feel unloving toward my parent.
___ I feel misunderstood by my parent.
___ I feel unloved by my parent.

EXERCISE 23A–CHECKLIST–NEGATIVE CONSEQUENCES OF PROTECTIONS (Cont'd)

D.   Negative Consequences at Work
with Employees/Employer/Partner
___ I'm involved in one or several power struggles at work.
___ I lack interest and motivation.
___ I feel manipulated.
___ I feel resistant, rebellious.
___ I feel angry, annoyed, and/or resentful.
___ I feel critical, judgmental.
___ I feel used, taken advantage of.
___ I feel unappreciated and/or unimportant.
___ I feel isolated.
___ I feel inadequate and/or scared.
___ I feel trapped.
___ I'm chronically late.
___ My employee is often late.
___ My employee or partner is resistant.
___ My employee or partner has lost initiative and motivation.

E.   Negative Consequences to Yourself
___ I am frequently ill.
___ I repeat similar patterns in my relationships.
___ I have difficulty in connecting with others.
___ I'm attracted to people who are unavailable.
___ I'm alone. I feel isolated.
___ I have low self-esteem, feel inadequate and unlovable.
___ I feel tension, fear, anxiety, frustration, anger, guilt.
___ I feel depressed, deadened, apathetic, sad, bored.
___ I feel unloving.
___ I feel manipulated.
___ I feel smothered.
___ I feel rejected.
___ I often experience a lack of commitment in relationships.
___ I have low creativity.
___ I lack joy.
___ I feel powerless.

EXERCISE 23B–CHECKLIST–SELF-LIMITING BELIEFS ABOUT PROTECTIONS AND CONSEQUENCES

Now that you've completed all the exercises on protections and consequences, go over this checklist very carefully. Remember that ALL these statements are erroneous. Each one that you checked is worthy of many hours of exploration.

PART 1: Protections

_____ 1. My protections will eventually get me what I want.
_____ 2. My protections work to avoid pain.
_____ 3. My protections are not unloving.
_____ 4. It's possible to be protected and still be intimate and connected.
_____ 5. It's possible to be protected and open to learning at the same time.
_____ 6. It's possible to be protected and feel happy.
_____ 7. It's possible to be protected without eroding my self-esteem.
_____ 8. It's possible to be protected and feel adequate.
_____ 9. It's possible to be protected and feel lovable.
_____ 10. Being unprotected leaves me too vulnerable.
_____ 11. If I'm open and loving people will take advantage of me.
_____ 12. Being soft and open is being weak. People will think less of me.
_____ 13. Being protected feels good.
_____ 14. Being protected is really taking care of myself.
_____ 15. Being protected has no negative consequences.
_____ 16. There is no other way to be in this crazy world but to be protected.
_____ 17. I have to protect because people don't care about me.
_____ 18. Being protected is the way I can feel powerful.
_____ 19. When I protect I'm owning my personal power.
_____ 20. It's important to be protected in order to teach the other person a lesson. If I'm not protected, others will think they can get away with their unloving behavior.

EXERCISE 23B–CHECKLIST–SELF-LIMITING BELIEFS
ABOUT PROTECTIONS AND CONSEQUENCES (Cont'd)

PART 2: Consequences

___ 1. My feelings are not a result of my own choices. My feelings are a result of how other people treat me.

___ 2. My unhappiness is caused by how others treat me.

3. It's my partner's, or my parents, or someone else's fault that:
   ___ I have a lousy sex life.
   ___ I have no fun.
   ___ I have no intimacy in my life.
   ___ I'm alone.
   ___ I have no money.
   ___ We never talk.
   ___ My kids are screwed up.
   ___ I never have time for myself.
   ___ I'm unhappy.
   ___ I feel bad about myself.
   ___ I'm overweight.
   ___ I'm always late.
   ___ I'm a failure.
   ___ I'm sick a lot.

4. It's my fault or I'm no good because:
   ___ I don't like my life.
   ___ I can't change.
   ___ I'm not happy.
   ___ I'm so judgmental and critical.
   ___ People don't like me.
   ___ I'm not successful

5. Fill in your own:

   ___
   ___
   ___
   ___

DO YOU ACT - OR REACT?

Condensed from
The Chicago Daily News
Sidney J. Harris

I walked with my friend, a Quaker, to the newsstand the other night, and he bought a paper, thanking the newsie politely. The newsie didn't even acknowledge it.

"A sullen fellow, isn't he?" I commented.

"Oh, he's that way every night," shrugged my friend.

"Then why do you continue to be so polite to him?" I asked.

"Why not?" inquired my friend. "Why should I let him decide how I'm going to act?"

As I thought about this incident later, it occurred to me that the important word was "act." My friend acts towards people; most of us react towards them.

He has a sense of inner balance which is lacking in most of us; he knows who he is, what he stands for, how he should behave. He refuses to return incivility for incivility, because then he would no longer be in command of his own conduct.

When we are enjoined in the Bible to return good for evil, we look upon this as a moral injunction - which it is. But it is also a psychological prescription for our emotional health.

Nobody is unhappier than the perpetual reactor. His center of emotional gravity is not rooted within himself, where it belongs, but in the world outside him. His spiritual temperature is always being raised or lowered by the social climate around him, and he is a mere creature at the mercy of these elements.

Praise gives him a feeling of euphoria, which is false, because it does not last and it does not come from self-approval. Criticism depresses him more than it should, because it confirms his own secretly shaky opinion of himself. Snubs hurt him and the merest suspicion of unpopularity in any quarter rouses him to bitterness.

A serenity of spirit cannot be achieved until we become the masters of our own actions and attitudes. To let another determine whether we shall be rude or gracious, elated or depressed, is to relinquish control over our own personalities, which is ultimately all we possess. The only true possession is self-possession.

CHAPTER

· 7 ·

ACKNOWLEDGING AND RESPECTING FEAR

We've all been taught to believe it's wrong or weak to be afraid. Most of us know that we're afraid and we cover it with protections. When we compare ourselves to others, we believe we're the only ones who are afraid or others are less afraid than we are. Let's start with all our cards on the table and acknowledge that everyone has many deep fears. We have all come to believe that we're not good enough, not lovable enough, inadequate, not doing it right, or just plain hopeless. We're too much of this or not enough of that. From these beliefs come the fears of disapproval, rejection, abandonment, and domination that we protect ourselves from in relationships.

You may not want to believe it, but *everyone* suffers from the same fears–your spouse, boss, hero, the minister who guides you, the psychologist whose counsel you seek, the President in whom you put your trust. Some people hide their fears better than others and even attain success in spite of them, but when you know people intimately you discover that we're all in this thing together. Nobody's got it all together. The demons of self-doubt affect us all, especially in relationships.

You are not wrong for being afraid. How could it have been any other way? Even as adults, disapproval continues to feel like a life and death issue. You may often feel panic in the face of disapproval, and do a lot of things to avoid it.

Moving past your fears is very possible. You have already moved past many of them. Think of the things you have been afraid of in the past that no longer control your life. You were probably afraid the first day you went to school, drove a car, rode a bike, started a new job. You can move past many more fears too, but you will be seriously hampered if you judge yourself for being afraid. Be kind to yourself. Know that you always have very important reasons for your feelings, thoughts, and behavior and that looking at those important reasons without self-judgment will greatly accelerate your emotional growth. The important reasons behind your fears are always generated by your erroneous, self-limiting beliefs.

If you weren't afraid, you would be as open as you were when you were first born. When confronted with something, you wouldn't be concerned with being "wrong," you would react with curiosity. "Oh, that's interesting. I wonder why you're feeling that way? And what do I have to learn in this situation? What's my lesson here?"

You could approach any situation in your life with that kind of curiosity if you weren't afraid of being wrong. But you close to learning, especially to learning about yourself, when you fear looking inside and finding out things about yourself that you think are really bad, really awful. Or you fear finding out things that you don't like about your feelings for other people.

Most of us spend a great deal of energy hiding the part within us that we believe is ugly or bad. Very often our closedness is a result of fearing that this "bad" part is proof that we're no good, that we did "it," that we're to blame and it's all our fault. Since we don't want it to be all our fault, we close down and point our finger at the other person, saying "It's all YOUR fault." We focus on trying to get others to look inward so we won't have to. To be open to learning, you must be ready to say "OK, I'm willing for it to be all my responsibility." You must be willing to let go of trying to get the other person to "see" anything and take 100% responsibility for what you do and for your unhappiness. Then you can be truly open to learning.

Having stopped yourself from saying "Well, she's got a part in this" or "If it weren't for him..." or "We're really equal in this," you will open to taking *total* responsibility for: "What's *my* lesson here? What do *I* need to learn? What's *my* part in this? How can I be a bit more committed, a bit wiser?" This is really difficult as long as you believe that "being responsible" means "being wrong." From this belief follows the fear that if you're wrong, then the other person isn't going to love you and you'll lose something of value–yourself or the other person. All of us have a little tiny child inside that still believes that if we aren't loved, we can't survive. When we experience conflict, and someone is angry or upset with us, we become five years old and that little kid inside says "Uh oh. I'm wrong, I'm bad, it's my fault, they're going to be angry, they're going to abandon me and I'm going to *die*." We desperately cling to the false belief that if someone rejects us, we can't handle it. This in turn creates the false belief that our unhappiness is tied to the other person, rather than to our own way of being in the world.

Our deepest fears and false beliefs are triggered in the relationships that are most important to us. All our protections come from the fear of this person who has a power similar to our parents'. (You probably give power to anyone who has an important part in your life.) Therefore, when any of these important people disapprove of you, those fears are touched off. Most people find it much easier to be open to learning anywhere *other* than in their important relationships. With your children, you're different than you are with other people's children. Grandparents are usually different with their grandchildren than they were with their children. Primary relationships are a fertile ground in which to learn and, at the same time, the most difficult place to learn.

EXERCISE 24–FEARS ABOUT RELATIONSHIPS WITH OTHER PEOPLE

1. Think about the fears you have regarding relationships in general or in some of the particular relationships in your life.

2. Complete any or all of the following sentences:

    "Some of the fears I have about being in a relationship are..."

    "Some of the fears I have about my relationship with_____are..."

    "Some of the fears I have about being in a relationship with my boss, peers, siblings, parents or children are..."

If you are alone, you can speak your thoughts or write them down. Do as many as you can in five minutes.

If you have a partner, you can do this out loud together. Your partner will say one of his/her fears, then you'll say one of yours and go back and forth like that for ten minutes. Don't analyze, therapize, discuss, or caretake.

DEMONSTRATION OF FEAR EXERCISE

A fear I have about being in a relationship with my husband is that everything is going to be up to me; that if we're going to be connected or if we're going to learn, that it's always going to be up to me, it will be all my responsibility.

A fear I have about being in relationship with my wife is that she is too powerful and she'll be in control of the situation because she talks about her feelings easier than I do, and if we get into talking about feelings, I will be overwhelmed.

A fear that I had when I was a kid about being in relationships with my friends was that I was going to be left out, that I wasn't important enough to be included.

EXERCISE 25–EXPLORING FEARS OF INADEQUACY

Some of the most devastating erroneous beliefs you got in childhood had to do with your adequacy. Everyone has some things about themselves–looks, feelings, thoughts, certain behaviors–which they hide because they feel there's something wrong with them. You developed feelings of inadequacy in childhood when your natural expressions were met with disapproval. When you heard, "You mean, *that* hurt your feelings?" or "I'll give you something to cry about," you came to believe you were too sensitive. When you heard, "Calm down, don't get so excited," or "You ask too many questions," you came to believe there was something wrong with you for feeling as you did or for your curiosity. When you expressed your natural sexual curiosity you got negative messages about that. In your curiosity to know things you may have broken things, and that brought disapproval. You forgot things and were made wrong. Many things about your way of being seemed wrong because they didn't fit what the bigger people around you believed was the right way to be. How often did you get the message that when you wanted to go to sleep was wrong, how much you wanted to eat was wrong, what you wanted to wear was wrong, what you thought was wrong, how you expressed yourself was wrong? There was a right way to do everything and you were often not doing it. To be lovable often meant to be exactly what the adults around you expected you to be. To be lovable meant to be perfect (by their standards/beliefs) and you didn't measure up.

The messages you received were often nonverbal. You may have gotten a feeling that something was wrong rather than hearing the words. The messages may not have always come from your parents, but from other significant people in your life–siblings, grandparents, other relatives, teachers and friends as well as from books, television or radio. We all came to conclusions about our inadequacy. There was a right way to think, feel, act, and look and we weren't cutting it. We decided many things early in our lives about how to adjust to being imperfect, unlovable, inadequate and wrong.

Go deep inside and ask yourself: What messages did I receive in my childhood? Maybe no one ever said you were wrong. Maybe you just concluded them from what your parents did or didn't do. Maybe the message you got was "I'll love you if you are good," or "You're not good enough because you are a girl," or "You've always been nothing but trouble," or "You are *so* lazy." Remember how you felt about those messages. Did they hurt? Did they make you angry? Did they make you want to hide? How are those messages still affecting you today? Are you acting out those same childhood roles? Are you still a good little girl? Are you still a trouble maker? Are you still an underachiever? Stop and let yourself feel now....

Now complete the questions on the following page.

EXERCISE 25A–EXPLORING BELIEFS ABOUT FEARS OF INADEQUACY

1. Do I fear being seen as:

A failure	Successful	Sick
Wrong	Inadequate	Unacceptable
Incompetent	Unmasculine	Immature
Crazy	Unfeminine	Neurotic
Stupid, dumb	Selfish	Foolish
Ugly	Boring	Closed
Shy, timid	Intense	

2. Do I believe that another person will not meet my needs because I'm:

Unworthy	Inadequate	Unlovable
Incompetent	Too poor	Not good enough

3. What messages did I get in childhood about being good or bad, right or wrong, okay or not okay?

4. What do I believe isn't good enough about me now? Do I feel inadequate physically, intellectually, emotionally, socially? Do I believe there's something wrong with my personality, that I'm not creative enough, or that I don't have a sense of humor?

5. Do I feel unsure of myself because:

    a. I believe I am not as intelligent, verbal, wealthy, attractive, interesting, independent, creative, social, open, important as my partner, as other people, or as I should be?

    b. I am too old, young, sensitive, intense, timid?

6. Are these beliefs causing me pain?

    How do I protect from the pain of these beliefs?

7. Why do I continue to believe this way? What am I afraid would happen if I let go of these beliefs?

165

EXERCISE 25B–CHECKLIST–SELF-LIMITING BELIEFS ABOUT ADEQUACY AND LOVABILITY

___ 1. I'm not adequate.

___ 2. I'm not lovable.

___ 3. I'm not good enough.

___ 4. My adequacy, lovability, feelings of self-worth and self-esteem come from other people liking or approving of me.

___ 5. I'm inadequate, unlovable or not good enough because:

___ I'm too tall.

___ I'm too short.

___ I'm too thin.

___ I'm too fat.

___ I'm ugly, homely, or unattractive.

___ I'm not intelligent enough.

___ I'm not creative enough.

___ I don't have a good sense of humor.

___ I don't make enough money.

___ I don't drive a nice car.

___ I'm shy.

___ I'm too aggressive.

___ I'm too selfish.

___ I'm too intense.

___ I'm too much, but I'm not sure what I'm too much of.

___ I'm too intelligent.

___ I'm too different.

___ I'm weird.

___ I'm too scattered.

___ I make mistakes.

___ I have physical defects or imperfections.

___ I have problems.

___ I cry too easily.

___ I'm too emotional.

___ I'm not perfect.

___ I'm not very verbal.

___ I don't think quickly enough.

___ I don't agree with you.

___ I'm just like my father.

EXERCISE 25B–CHECKLIST–SELF-LIMITING BELIEFS ABOUT ADEQUACY AND LOVABILITY (Cont'd)

___ I'm just like my mother.
___ I can't take care of myself.
___ I need a man to take care of me.
___ I need a woman to take care of me.
___ I can't make decisions.
___ I'll never amount to anything.
___ I can't tell good jokes.
___ I'm too serious.
___ I'm not serious enough.
___ I'm too sensitive.
___ I'm too insensitive.
___ I always make a bad first impression.
___ I think differently than other people.
___ I'm a loner.
___ I don't have a partner.
___ I'm afraid to be alone.
___ I have fears.
___ I have phobias.
___ I'm immature.
___ I'm not a professional.
___ I never went to college.
___ I didn't graduate high school.
___ I have a lousy vocabulary.
___ I can't do math.

___ I don't read well.
___ I have too much imagination.
___ I have no imagination.
___ I'm too spiritual.
___ I'm not spiritual enough.
___ I can't do anything right.
___ When bad things happen, it's always my fault.
___ Bad things always happen to me.
___ I'm a compulsive overeater.
___ I'm an alcoholic.
___ I'm a drug addict.
___ I'm crazy.
___ I'm a phony.
___ I'm righteous and arrogant.
___ I'm depressed.
___ I'm lazy.
___ I'm superficial.
___ I'm screwed up.
___ I'm not important.
___ I'm boring, not interesting
___ I'm second rate
___ I have no personality
___ I'm a goody-goody.
___ I'm stupid.
___ I don't want to be in a committed relationship.

WOMEN
___ My breasts are too small.
___ My breasts are too large.
___ My vagina is ugly.
___ My thighs are too big.
___ My_____is too_____

MEN
___ My penis is too small.
___ My penis is too big.
___ My_____is too_____

(This might be a good time to go back to Chapter 4, Page 94 and use the Format For Challenging Beliefs.)

EXERCISE 25C–FEARS ABOUT LEARNING

1. Take a minute to look inside. Think about what you are afraid is wrong with you: your imperfections; your fear of being wrong; what you feel inadequate about; your fears about being inadequate, not enough, not important, not lovable. Think about what you protect yourself from knowing about yourself.

2. Complete the following sentence:

    "A fear I have about being open to learning about myself is..."

Example: A fear that I have about being open to learning about myself is that I'm going find out I'm wrong, and wrong means bad, unlovable. It is going to confirm that there really is something bad or unlovable about me, and that's why I have difficulty in being open to learning. (Keep expanding into the depths of your feelings and beliefs.)

EXERCISE 26–EXPLORING FEAR OF PAIN

A great deal of our behavior boils down to trying to avoid pain. There is going to be some pain in being open. As long as you believe you can't handle it, you have to close to learning.

In their well-meaning but often misguided attempts to be loving, parents often give many verbal and nonverbal messages that it is bad or wrong to be in pain and/or that their children can't handle deep pain. Attempts to smooth over painful events by getting children to stop feeling their pain, glossing over it, trying to make it better, all communicate that it is not right to feel pain and that "You can't handle your own pain." When parents fall apart when their children are hurt or scared, they communicate that they can't handle their children's pain, and therefore the child must avoid or not show pain.

It is very rare for parents to caringly communicate that they have confidence that their children can find their way through pain and learn from it.

What are your fears of being in pain? If you were to let yourself really open to deep pain, for example the pain of rejection, what is your belief about that pain? That you'll go crazy? That you can't handle it? That it will overwhelm you?

The truth is that you can handle a great deal of pain and you don't have to be afraid of it. The thought of being in pain is worse than the reality, but until you test out your beliefs about pain you are stuck in protecting yourself.

Go on to the following page to complete this exercise.

EXERCISE 26A–FORMAT FOR EXPLORING BELIEFS ABOUT FEAR OF PAIN

Do you fear feeling:

Afraid	Hurt	Disappointed
Humiliated	Weak	Grieved
Criticized	Disoriented	Insecure
Put-down	Despairing	Off Balance
Judged	Vulnerable	Violated
Devastated	Out of control	Not in control of others
Rejected	Discounted	Abandoned
Helpless	Lonely	Disoriented
Dominated	Controlled	Left out
Needy	Shut out	Found out

Do you fear:

Loss of love	Loss of relationship
Loss of self	Knowing your partner's deepest feelings
Loss of face	Knowing yourself
Intimacy	

1. What am I afraid will happen if I open to my pain?

    ___I'll die.
    ___I'll go crazy.
    ___I'll kill myself.
    ___I'll be weak, a wimp, one down.
    ___I'll be rejected and be in even more pain.
    ___I'll lose myself, get taken advantage of, be controlled.
    ___I'll cry and it's stupid to cry.
    ___I'll be in pain forever. The pain will be unending.

2. What childhood messages and experiences brought about these beliefs?

3. How do I avoid feeling my primary pain?

4. What consequences result from my avoiding pain?

EXERCISE 26B–CHECKLIST–SELF-LIMITING BELIEFS ABOUT PAIN

___ 1.   No one really wants to hear my pain.

___ 2.   No one can handle the depth of my pain.

___ 3.   People will think less of me if they see me cry.

___ 4.   If I let go to my pain, it will be unending.

___ 5.   I can't handle pain.

___ 6.   Showing pain is a sign of weakness.

___ 7.   If I cry, I will be rejected.

___ 8.   If I cry, I will be weak and I will fall apart.

___ 9.   Once I start to cry, I'll never stop.

___ 10. If I open to my pain, I will go crazy.

___ 11. If I open to my pain, I will die.

___ 12. My problems are so trivial compared to other people's that I have no right to be in pain.

___ 13. I can't handle the pain of rejection.

___ 14. Getting rejected is a pain worse than death.

___ 15. If I open to my pain people will think I'm crazy.

___ 16. There's no point in opening to pain. It doesn't make anything better. There's no point in crying over spilled milk.

___ 17. Opening to pain is dumb. It's a waste of time.

EXERCISE 27–TRUE COMMUNICATION

Underneath your protections is your true communication. It's the part of yourself that would speak with the honesty of a little child. It's the soft, frightened, vulnerable part that just wants to be heard and acknowledged and appreciated, but is too afraid to ask for what it needs or to give it. It's not your Higher Self, but is a part of you that opens the doorway to it. It's the lovable part of you that is most often judged as weak. It's the part you are afraid to show for fear you will be controlled if you show it and feel it.

Remember a time in your life when you reacted protectively either to someone trying to control you or when someone did something that upset you...a time when someone you loved was hurt by what you said to her, a time you got angry and scared your child or your partner or a friend. Recall a time when you expressed a lot of anger to someone you care for. Recall as many of the details as you can: where the situation occurred; what the circumstances were. And feel inside how terrible it felt to get angry, how trapped you felt by your own anger and how frustrated you must have been, not knowing what else to do. And ask yourself, "What was I *really* feeling under that anger? What did I really want to say to that person? If I could have been in touch with my heart, what did my heart feel and want to say to that person?" Did you want to say, "I'm afraid I'll lose you"? Did you want to say, "It scares me when you come home late and I don't know where you are"? Did you want to say, "I'm afraid I'm not good enough when you pull away from me," or "I get scared you don't love me when you don't want to touch me?" Look inside and see what you really wanted to say.... Stop, close your eyes, and feel what has gone unexpressed far too long.

Feel how much your heart longs to talk to the people you have loved, and the people you love, and to tell them what you are really feeling underneath the protections, underneath the walls. Feel how good it would be to hold them and let your heart really speak. And now is your chance to do that.

EXERCISE 27–FORMAT FOR TRUE COMMUNICATION

1.   Think of a conflict in which you've reacted by wanting to control another and either write or describe the situation out loud as if the other person were really there.

2.   After describing the situation, describe what you really felt and what you really wanted to say.

Example: The incident was when I came home very excited from a conference I had attended and my husband was shut down and nonresponsive. I became very irritated and angry with him, calling him names and threatening to just not be around him when he was like that.

What I really felt was sad and alone. What I really wanted to say to him was, "When you're nonresponsive it really feels awful. I feel as if all the wind is let out of my sails. I feel alone and scared that you don't like who I am. I don't know if it's that you don't like my being so enthusiastic or if what I'm actually saying upsets you. I get so confused and feel tense in my whole body."

3.   Remember and write as many incidents as you can and become more and more aware of how you feel under your protections.

4.   If you want to share the incidents with the person who was involved, check yourself to see whether your intention is to learn more about yourself and the very good reasons the other person had for reacting as he did or whether you want the other person to feel guilty and wrong. If your intention is to get something from the other person, expect a defensive reaction.

EXERCISE 28–TELLING THE TRUTH

Telling the truth is one of the most difficult things to do. We continually deny the truth, withhold or distort it, because of our fears that other people can't handle it, may leave us emotionally or physically, or that we don't have the right to feel as we do or want what we want.

For example, many people stay in emotionally or physically abusive situations without telling the truth. The truth is "When you behave this way, I don't like being around you." It may be difficult to realize that when someone is being abusive, the loving behavior is to confront that person and not let the person believe that it is working. Instead, we go right to our protections, withdrawing, attempting to placate, or becoming combative.

In what areas are you not being truthful? Have you made love when you haven't been turned on, had an affair or are having an affair without telling your partner, are you bored or not feeling respectful of your partner's choices? Are you feeling your boss or employee or child is taking advantage of you? What are the consequences of not telling the truth? How do you wind up feeling about yourself? What happens between you and the other person?

Not telling the truth guarantees staying stuck. The truth shakes things up, but it is the only chance that you both have to learn and grow. Speaking the truth is the loving thing to do. Your partner may not respond to your truth as the gift that it is. He may be too scared, but you'll never know that until you are honest.

If you approach another from a place of fear, then in all probability, you will receive a defensive reaction. The fact that your own protective barriers are up is reflected by an edge in your tone of voice and a closedness in your body language. If you fear a hostile reaction, then you will probably approach another with your own defensiveness. But if you approach that person with your softness and openness–open to understanding and accepting the other's reaction and open to sharing with that person your own feelings–then you have a much better chance of receiving openness in return.

In the face of your best efforts to remain open and loving, others may still retreat into being self-righteous victims. What then? Telling them the truth and doing what you want and know is right will be risky. Will they remain closed? Will they eventually open to you again? Nobody can assure you of other people's reactions. But what choices do you have? If you don't tell them, they may seem happy, but you'll be miserable. You'll feel imprisoned by your relationships and eventually resent the relationships and dislike yourself. Keeping secrets usually injures intimacy. Honesty is risky and often leads to problems. But confronting the truth can lead both of you to even better relationships and to greater self-esteem for you.

Hearing the truth is equally difficult. For example, if you want honesty, and you want to learn with your children, you have to be willing to hear that they may be doing various things you consider wrong, like taking drugs or having sex. Do you want to hear why they lie to you? You have to be willing to hear that maybe your punitive or judgmental reaction has created a situation where people around you don't tell you the truth. Do you want to learn about yourself or do you just want to be angry because the person has lied to you?

Very often when children lie, the parents see the child as wrong. But in order to effectively deal with it, you have to be open to learning about what *you* are doing that makes the child afraid of being honest with you.

No one can tell you how much you should say or when to speak the truth about how you feel. One of our favorite sayings is, "All important decisions must be made on the basis of insufficient data." You can never know for sure how another will react. You can only have faith that whatever happens, you have the power, if not alone, then with a little help from your friends, to learn from any situation and turn it from a problem into an opportunity.

Having the intention to learn must be your highest priority. When you realize that the intention to learn is what will bring you all the "highs" in your life–joy, happiness, love, intimacy–and that the intention to protect is what ruins everything, then you will naturally begin to make learning your highest priority. When learning becomes more important than protecting against being wrong, losing, failure, ridicule–higher than anything that you want to protect against–then you can begin to move.

EXERCISE 28–FORMAT FOR TELLING THE TRUTH

When doing this exercise with a partner:

Sit facing each other.

Person revealing Truth:

> "A truth about myself (an action, a feeling, a belief) that I've never told you is..."

Person receiving Truth:

1. "What I'd like to explore and understand about your truth is..."

2. "How I'm feeling about what you've told me is..."

3. "What I need to explore and understand about my own feelings is..."

If you are working with a person you are in a relationship with, then you can use this truth as a basis for exploration.

If you are not working with someone you are in a relationship with, first tell the truth as if the other person is your parent, mate, child, etc.; then explore with your partner your fear and beliefs in telling the truth to that person.

When doing this exercise alone:

1. Complete the following sentence in as much detail as you can:

   "A truth about myself (an action, a feeling, a belief) that I've never shared with anyone is..."

2. What are the negative consequences of not admitting this truth–the negative effects that it has had on your feelings about yourself, the other person, and on your relationship?

LET GO

To "let go" does not mean to stop caring, it means I can't do it for someone else.

To "let go" is not to cut myself off, it's the realization I can't control another.

To "let go" is not to enable, but allow learning from natural consequences.

To "let go" is to admit powerlessness, which means the outcome is not in my hands.

To "let go" is not to try to change or blame another, it's to make the most of myself.

To "let go" is not to care for, but to care about.

To "let go" is not to fix, but to be supportive.

To "let go" is not to judge, but to allow another to be a human being.

To "let go" is not to be in the middle arranging all the outcomes, but to allow others to affect their destinies.

To "let go" is not to be protective, it's to permit another to face reality.

To "let go" is not to deny, but to accept.

To "let go" is not to nag, scold or argue, but instead to search out my own shortcomings and correct them.

To "let go" is not to adjust everything to my desires but to take each day as it comes and cherish myself in it.

To "let go" is not to criticize or regulate anybody, but to try to become what I dream I can be.

To "let go" is not to regret the past, but to grow and live for the future.

To "let go" is to fear less and love more.

—ANONYMOUS

CHAPTER

·8·

HEALING

Emotional abuse–being slighted, ridiculed, dismissed, put down, criticized, rejected, made fun of, teased–is rampant in most people's relationships and is even thought by some to be helpful and loving.

Abusive experiences are compounded in childhood either by having to hide the hurt and suffer alone, or being further abused for showing the hurt. Being told that there is something wrong with you for your reactions ("There, there, it's not so bad," "You mean that hurt your feelings?!" "You're bigger than that, just rise above it," "Come on, lets go get an ice cream," "I'll give you something to cry about!" "What's the matter, can't you take a joke?") leaves deep scars. A child's protections are attempts to get some needed relief from pain and to avoid wounding experiences in the future.

As adults, we are still acting out the same patterns. Have you ever berated yourself with variations on this theme: "You're such a jerk, what's wrong with you?" Judgments and disrespect are so much a part of our way of life that we rarely stop to consider the devastating effects on ourselves and others. Protections are the scars that cover the deep wounds of emotional abuse. Healing those wounds is possible and an important part of becoming more open to learning. But the healing can only happen when you stop being a victim.

In Chapter 6 we discussed two ways to be in pain: a blaming, victim pain and a nonblaming pain. Recall that victim pain is the "poor me" pain that says, "You're making me miserable." This shifts responsibility to others. No learning can take place, and the blaming person is stuck, as is anyone who buys into that blame.

When you experience nonblaming pain, you feel the sadness appropriate to the situation, accept your responsibility for whatever part you had in creating the situation, and move on to learning something about yourself.

For example, people caught up in victim pain blame their parents (and others) for their unhappiness. Those who don't blame understand that their parents were doing the best job they could. Their parent's actions were the products of their erroneous beliefs and no one is to blame. The situation is sad, terribly sad, as we all missed out on getting and giving the love that we could have had in our growing up years. We have been damaged and need to do some repair work, but that work can bring us into a clearer and better place. We can damn our parents (and others) or we can be thankful that we have the capacity to help ourselves. If we're really lucky, we have people around us who care enough to help us in our relearning process.

Important healing takes place when you feel compassion for those who have been hurt by your protections, your sadness over their being hurt, and your forgiveness of yourself and others. Harboring resentment, anger, and blame is not helpful in your own healing process. Forgiveness of others releases you from your own self-blame, and when released from blame, your self-esteem rises, you feel less protected and more loving.

Compassion

Compassion is that feeling you get when you climb into another person's skin and feel as they must feel. You can do this, because others feel as you do. The key is to be more in touch with your own feelings. You are most blocked from knowing others' feelings because you don't want to know your own. You don't want to know that your criticism, sarcasm, icy withdrawal, raging anger–any behavior that produces guilt or fear in another–is painful to that person. If you faced this, even though you are not responsible for another's feelings, you would feel bad, and it would be much harder to continue that behavior. You want to be protected and believe that your protections don't have an effect. And that's just not true. You also don't want to know how painful other's protections are to you.

You want to believe that you can take it, and little things like sarcasms or criticisms, or slights don't hurt you. But that's not true either. All human beings are very sensitive and have many beliefs that create a great deal of pain. The amount of pain that's dished out is awesome. We have all had to protect against feeling this pain, and the truth is that it affects us all.

It doesn't feel good to another person to be in your energy when you are protected. If that person were an enlightened human being who didn't have any erroneous beliefs and therefore never took anything personally, you couldn't hurt him. The fact is that none of us are there yet. Others do feel hurt by your protections, even though it is not your fault that they feel that way. Whenever anyone feels hurt, it is his responsibility. Nevertheless, it *is* your responsibility to realize that this child, mate, employee, or parent in front of you is not an ideally enlightened human being but somebody with fears and beliefs, and that your negative energy is going to feel painful to them. So that is what you are dealing with here–the fact, the reality, that your protections do feel painful to other people.

Sadness

Sadness is the feeling that occurs when, without blaming yourself or others, you realize the mess your protections have created . To feel sad without feeling guilty or wrong is not easy, but it is possible and necessary if you are to move forward. You protect when you feel wrong and/or guilty and that keeps you from feeling the vulnerable feelings of sadness. Without accepting and feeling that sadness, you can't move on to the next step which is forgiveness.

Forgiveness

Forgiveness occurs as a natural event when you feel your non-blaming sadness. There is, in fact, no one to blame. We all act from a great deal of ignorance and the fear that our erroneous beliefs have created. We are not basically mean, malicious people, but when frightened, we become the very people we have sworn not to be. Forgiveness is the key that allows you to go forth in the world with true compassion and love, to become the loving person that you are capable of being. It is the key to spreading this love so that our planet can be healed.

Forgiveness as generally understood is a process in which I forgive you for being wrong. This is a subtle form of condescension, attack and manipulation. Therefore, as popular as it is, it cannot be true forgiveness. True forgiveness is an awareness that apparent attacks aren't what they seem to be. True forgiveness is the acknowledgement that what looks like an attack is actually a call for love, help or learning. Anytime I feel as if I'm being attacked, I have forgotten the truth that lives under the perceived attack, probably because my own wounds are making it difficult to remember. But the bottom line is that you can never truly attack me emotionally, spiritually or psychologically. And therefore the process of true forgiveness entails the recognition that if you never attacked me, there is nothing I need to forgive you for. How could I forgive you for having emotional wounds, for being afraid, for feeling guilty, for being in pain? What is there to forgive?

True forgiveness is a paradox. If I forgive you for what you never did, there's nothing to forgive you for. The acknowledgement that there is nothing to forgive you for is precisely what true forgiveness is.

EXERCISE 29–COMPASSION, SADNESS AND FORGIVENESS

This is an exercise in compassion and healing. You have been through a lot in doing the exercises in this book, and some of you may be hard on yourselves and/or on other people. You may be feeling upset with your parents, your mate, your kids, or yourself about unloving behaviors. Letting go of the blame and feeling your compassion and forgiveness for yourself and others is the purpose of this exercise.

This exercise will be in three parts, and it will take about an hour.

Part 1 is designed to increase your understanding of what another person really feels. You will name the person you believe is hurting or has hurt as a result of your protections. Then you become that person, and you talk as that person. You complete the sentences: "Someone who has been hurt by my ....(name your protection) is............" (Fill in the person's name.) "Now I'm going to become.........."(Say the person's name again.) Then BECOME that person and speak as that person must feel being at the other end of your protections. The best way to do that is to keep your eyes closed so you can go inside and really become the person on the other end of your protections. Read the following demonstrations, then read the visualization, and then do Part 1. We suggest that you do Part 1 for at least fifteen minutes.

When you have finished Part 1, you will go to Part 2 of the exercise, which is also demonstrated. This is about feeling your own sadness caused by your behavior, your protections. Part 2 will take five to ten minutes.

Part 3 entails just reading some ideas about forgiveness.

Demonstration - One person doing exercise alone

JORDAN: Someone I've hurt with my icy withdrawal is my son Eric. Now I'm going to become Eric.

183

EXERCISE 29–COMPASSION, SADNESS AND FORGIVENESS
(Cont'd)

> (as Eric) "Dad, when I do something that you don't like and you get silent, I really get scared. I'm so afraid to do anything that upsets you because I don't want you to be angry with me. I feel awful when you withdraw. I feel you don't love me and I'm scared that you won't love me unless I'm exactly what you think I should be. I feel as if I have no room to be me, to mess up. I'm scared around you a lot of the time. I really want you to love me and I really try. Please love me."

Once you have finished being that person think of another person you have hurt with one of your protections and become him or her. You can speak as your parents, children, present mate, ex-mate, employees, anyone whom you have hurt. They can even be people who are deceased. After you have become as many people as you can think of, you are ready for the next part of the exercise.

Demonstration - Two people doing the exercise together

To do this exercise with a partner, you will alternate one person at a time. The alternating turns work as follows, for example: Margie identifies one of her protections and the person who was hurt; she then becomes that person. Next, Jordan identifies one of his protections and the person who was hurt and he becomes that person. Once they each have done that, it goes back to Margie and she does a second one. Then Jordan does a second one. Then she does a third one and when she finishes, so does he.

The demonstration will only show one cycle, but you will do as many people in as many different situations in your life as you can think of in fifteen minutes.

EXERCISE 29–COMPASSION, SADNESS AND FORGIVENESS
(Cont'd)

MARGIE: Someone I've hurt with my being irritated and parental is my husband Jordan. Now I'm going to become Jordan.

(As Jordan) "Margie, when you get that parental edge, that irritated quality, that hard edge in your voice, it feels like you are telling me that I've done it wrong and it is one of the worst feelings. It feels like you're telling me that I don't care about you and that you believe that I don't care about you. I feel really awful because I know how much I love you, and I know how important you are to me, and I know how hard I try to let you know that. When you have that irritation and that quality in your voice that says I'm wrong, I just feel so bad. I feel so unseen. I know that I get uptight, but what I'm feeling inside is a deep pain inside my stomach, because it feels like you just don't see how much I love you."

JORDAN: The person I've hurt with my defensiveness and my closedness to learning is my wife Margie. Now I'll become Margie.

(As Margie) "Jordan, you know that the most important thing to me in my life is learning about things. What I've always wanted is for somebody to want to learn about themselves and me as much as I've been interested in learning about them and learning about myself. And what I really feel sad about is all of the opportunities that we've missed to create a wonderful intimacy between us because you've been threatened by what I wanted to do or what I was thinking about. I feel such a sadness that we haven't created together what I know is possible for us to have created together. I'm sad that I haven't had someone there for me the way I know that I

EXERCISE 29–COMPASSION, SADNESS AND FORGIVENESS
(Cont'd)

> can be there for other people. It leaves me feeling so empty sometimes, shut out, left out and sad that we haven't created the intimacy, and sad that I don't get to have that kind of connection with other people. I guess I feel mostly sad about the things that I've missed with you in not having that kind of connection."

VISUALIZATION–COMPASSION AND EMPATHY

The following visualization will help you do Part 1 by getting in touch with your feelings. Choose a quiet, comfortable place. Read the visualization silently and slowly allow the words to sink in and the feelings to flow. If you are doing this with a partner, one of you will probably finish reading first. Remember, this isn't a competition. Take your time and allow the memories to come up. Whoever finishes first should just continue recalling incidents and feelings until your partner is ready.

Take some nice deep breaths, and just relax...Let your awareness go inside. Go back in your memory and remember a time you hurt someone you loved...you hurt him/her very much. Maybe you didn't mean to, but you did...You pushed him/her away, or you said angry words, or you put a wall up between you. Where were you? Who else was around? Imagine how that person must have felt...Let yourself feel his/her feelings for a moment, and imagine how he/she felt...Did he/she feel afraid of you? Did he/she feel as if you'd abandoned him/her? Did he/she feel as if you had broken his/her heart? If he/she could have talked to you, what would he/she have said? Open your heart and feel that person's feelings. Don't be afraid of the pain, just feel it. Let down the walls between yourself and that person and feel. Stop, close your eyes and give yourself time to remember and feel.

And now, take a deep breath and remember a time in your life when you did something to hurt one of your parents. How old

EXERCISE 29–COMPASSION, SADNESS AND FORGIVENESS
(Cont'd)

were you? Maybe you called your Mom names, maybe you pushed her away and ignored her. Maybe you didn't call your Dad or visit him...and he felt crushed inside, even if he didn't show you. Let yourself feel how he/she must have felt, what a failure he/she must have felt like, how sad he/she must have been. What would he/she have wanted to say to you? Allow yourself to feel the pain in his/her heart...Stop, close your eyes and let the images come.

And now, remember a more recent time in your life when you were in a relationship with someone and you hurt him/her very much... Maybe you put up a wall between you and he/she felt abandoned...Maybe you yelled at him/her...Maybe you rejected him/her sexually...Maybe you left him/her for someone else...Maybe you refused to comfort him/her...Allow yourself to feel how that person felt in his/her heart... Feel his/her pain, his/her hurt, because now it is time for you to experience compassion and open to love. Stop, close your eyes and feel.

And now turn the page and do Part 1.

EXERCISE 29–FORMAT FOR COMPASSION, SADNESS AND FORGIVENESS

PART 1

1. Begin by saying, "Someone I've hurt with my _____ (name the protection) is_____" (name the person).

2. Then you will become that person and say "Now I'm going to become _____" and feel yourself enter that person's heart, feel yourself inside of him or her and imagine that you are sitting across from yourself.

3. Be the person you've named and talk to yourself and tell yourself how hurt you are and what you really wanted.

4. And then if you're doing this with a partner, your partner will do the same thing and you will go back and forth until you complete in fifteen minutes. Go as deep as you can, with your eyes closed. And you can begin.

After fifteen minutes, go on to Part 2.

PART 2

1. Now become yourself again and speak to each of the people who you have just become and tell each of them your feelings about having hurt them.

Example: "Eric, I really feel awful at how many times I have hurt you. I know you try real hard and I really love you. I feel really bad that when I get upset that I act that way to you. I know how tense and awful it has made you feel. I really want to have a better relationship with you and I know the tension between us really gets in the way. I love you my son."

2. If you're doing this with a partner, alternately speak to each of the people you have just become and tell them your feelings about having hurt them. Take five to ten minutes for this part of the exercise.

After you have completed this process with all the people to whom you need to express your sadness, you can move on to the next part of the exercise.

EXERCISE 29–FORMAT FOR COMPASSION, SADNESS AND FORGIVENESS (Cont'd)

PART 3

For this part you will read out loud the following:

"As I look back now on all the times I have hurt those I've loved, I know that I was scared of getting hurt and all I was doing was protecting myself. I never meant to hurt all of those people and I know I had good reasons for doing what I did. I know that all I wanted was to be loved and understood, and that I am not bad, just frightened myself."

Now place your hands over your heart and say the following words out loud:

"I forgive myself for all the pain and hurt I have caused others. I release myself from any ways I have been punishing myself. I understand how frightened and protected I was, and I forgive myself and I love myself."

Breathe that forgiveness in, and feel it healing you inside and filling you up with peace.

And now think about all those people who have hurt you in your life and inflicted pain upon you and continue by speaking out loud the following:

"I see how everyone who has hurt me has never meant to hurt me just as I never meant to hurt others. I see how scared and protected they were, and that all they wanted was love, too. I can see that the little child was in my parents as well—the little child who didn't get the love he or she wanted growing up, and who got frightened and cold and then couldn't give me the love I needed either. Mom and Dad, I understand that you weren't loved the way you needed to be either, and I forgive you for not always knowing how to love me in

EXERCISE 29–FORMAT FOR COMPASSION, SADNESS AND FORGIVENESS (Cont'd)

the way I needed. I forgive you for hurting me. And I forgive myself for hurting you. And I feel the forgiveness connecting me to you wherever you are, and giving me peace. And I can now understand the unloved little child within my lovers or partners and see how they didn't mean to hurt me either, but they too were unloved and afraid. And I forgive them in my heart for hurting me. And as I think about all of us on this planet, and how frightened we are inside, and how we protect ourselves from being hurt again, and end up hurting others, I send a shower of forgiveness to all of humanity for being so scared, and for putting up the walls we do. I feel my commitment to love rather than to those walls, and to compassion rather than protection."

Sharing from the Workshop after Compassion Exercise

SHARING: I was surprised at the depth of the sadness. But I found out it wasn't inexhaustible. I didn't know that. Now I do, and that's real nice. There is a limit. I can let it go.

SHARING: I never understood this. I don't understand why I experience the kind of pain I felt here (and I was also kind of shocked at the depth of it) and have it be a really wonderful experience. It really felt good. I don't understand how pain at one time feels good and at other times it's awful.

MARGIE: Because the pain of the victim is a very helpless pain, it is a terrible pain to feel. But the pain of cleansing, which this is, cleansing pain, healing pain, learning pain, an existential pain, that kind of pain is very releasing, very healing when you go into it.

SHARING: It feels like it is moving out. Is it?

JORDAN: Yes, because you are releasing something from within you. It is inside, it's like a festering wound inside and there is a healing that happens when you move that out. The other pain is a victim pain, the pain of feeling helpless and powerless, and it never feels good.

SHARING: Now I know why I've come back here three times–the specialness of learning to come from loving yourself and putting yourself into the other person and being able to experience within me what that person must feel like when they're made wrong or talked down to, feeling my anger coming across to that person. Coming back and being able to experience me through the eyes of that person, I think is the most powerful exercise of all. It creates a lot of love for the other person and the other person loves it.

SHARING: I'm not quite sure what the fear that I had was, but I've felt really comfortable with this whole workshop until this exercise, and I couldn't do this one. I felt as if I had to have that person being there with me to be able to either act like them or...I'm in therapy because I want to be heard and I have some kind of block on trying to be somebody else.

MARGIE: Well, there's probably something to learn about that. About your fear of really feeling into what the other person is feeling. A lot of the times, if we are afraid to feel what they are feeling, it may be because you are afraid of acknowledging the consequences of your own behavior. I don't know, that's just a possibility, but there is some good reason why and that could be an important exploration for you.

SHARING: It felt as if you had to have a boyfriend or a husband in order to be able to do it.

MARGIE: That may be one of your limiting beliefs, because you've lived your whole life with relationships. You've had parents and perhaps siblings and friends and co-workers and in *all* of our relationships, sometimes we are protective. You may have a belief that the only time you can get into compassion and empathy is with a mate, which would be very limiting for you.

SHARING: I saw that the most important thing I need is the forgiveness of myself. Pain, fear, anger–they all wash away in that forgiveness. Thank you.

SHARING: I was finally able to say good-bye to my mother after three years.

JORDAN: So the forgiveness, and I think it's true for all of us, is really for us. It is freeing. People are afraid to forgive for fear that it is going to let the other person off the hook, that they are really giving in. That they are too miserable, to hurt to be able to forgive the person who "did it" to them. If you're having trouble letting go of it, there is some good reason why you're hanging onto it. It's important to know that letting go of it is not for them. It's for you.

EXERCISE 29A–CHECKLIST–LIMITING BELIEFS ABOUT FORGIVENESS

___ 1. I need to continue to punish myself so those I've hurt will suffer less.

___ 2. I need to punish myself to make sure that I don't keep doing the things that hurt myself and others.

___ 3. If I forgive my parents I will be too vulnerable and I will get hurt again.

___ 4. If I forgive my partner, he or she will never change.

___ 5. Forgiving myself is selfish and self-indulgent.

___ 6. Once I'm forgiven, then I'm absolved and I can protect again.

___ 7. If I forgive the people who hurt me, they will just keep hurting me.

___ 8. Forgiving myself and others makes me weak.

EXERCISE 30–HEALING CHILDHOOD PAIN

This is an exercise that needs to be done with another person. In one part, you will have the opportunity to heal your own pain. In the other, you will be helping another person heal his pain.

Your Own Pain

This exercise may help you relive some of your childhood pain and finally finish with it. We suggest that you do it with a loving partner, a caring therapist or a good friend. Pain can be healed in the presence of love. Experiencing deep pain alone is not advisable for most people because it merely replays the original incident. At the times in your past when you were in pain, the event itself was not nearly as problematic as the reactions of those around you. All of your sad feelings, from minor disappointments and rejections to tragic events such as the death of a parent or your parents' divorce, would not have caused the trauma they did if you could have experienced your deep pain in the presence of love and been allowed to continue feeling your feelings until you were through with them. The mourning period varies for each person, but eventually the pain would have been healed, you would have learned what you needed to learn from the situation, and you would have been done with it. Instead, most of us carry around deep pockets of pain that we have covered over and now must protect because of our fear of re-experiencing them.

Others' Pain

Helping others in pain requires your willingness to allow them to experience the depths of their pain while letting them know that you care about them. There are two ways to physically touch people when they are in pain. One way communicates your discomfort with pain and your desire to make it go away. The message communicated verbally or nonverbally is, "There, there, everything will be all right. Why don't you think of other things, happy things." The other communicates that you have faith that the person in pain has within himself the ability to feel deeply, learn from his pain and heal himself.

In order to really help another, you may have to clear up your own beliefs about pain and your beliefs about what another person who is in pain needs. To really help, you must believe that people don't need to have their pain "made better" or their problems solved. You are not responsible for fixing anybody else's pain. All you need to do is be there to listen and care about and respect that person's feelings.

EXERCISE 30–FORMAT FOR HEALING CHILDHOOD PAIN

Tell your partner exactly what you need him/her to do for you to feel cared for. How you need to be held or touched, what you need him/her to say or not say. You can become a little child and ask for the comforting you need. Your partner can say the loving things one says to a little child. You may also want to have a soft object to rub on your lips or face or a stuffed animal to hold onto. Anything that you need for your nurturing is okay.

This exercise will ask you to:

1. Recall a painful incident from your childhood and say "A time I felt hurt growing up was...."

2. And then say, "What I really wanted to say was...."

Example: A time I felt hurt growing up was when my parents left our farm in upstate New York to move to California, and I knew I wasn't going to see my Grandfather again. What I really wanted to say was, "Grandpa is the only person who loves me. I don't want to leave him. Please don't take me away. I love you Grandpa. I don't think I can live without you."

EXERCISE 30–FORMAT FOR HEALING CHILDHOOD PAIN
(Cont'd)

> 3. Let yourself sink deeply into your feelings and allow yourself to be healed with the love your partner is giving you.

Doing this exercise over and over again with the same and/or different issues in the presence of love will heal it. When you no longer have to protect against it you will have removed a button which, when pushed, used to bring up your protections.

On the next few pages, we have included long visualizations to help you bring deep feelings to the surface. Create a conducive environment to relax and feel safe; a quiet space with dim lighting is usually helpful. If music is on, make sure it is quiet and restful. Your partner will read the visualization slowly, taking time to allow your mind to drift back into time. The visualization will be useful in leading you into the above exercise.

"Begin by taking some nice, deep, relaxing breaths, right in the middle of your chest, and when you exhale, let all the tension go as you breathe out. If you are aware of any places in your body that are tense, breathe into those places. Relax and allow yourself to travel back now, way back as far as you can remember, back to a time when you were very small, a little girl or a little boy. Feel yourself turning back into that child right now, remember how you looked, and picture yourself looking that way. What was your favorite toy? Who were your friends? Just let your mind go, and feel that little child stirring inside of you. Remember a time when you were growing up, that something happened that hurt you… remember a time something or someone hurt you…recreate that time in your mind. Remember where you were, what was happening…who was with you…how were you feeling inside? Find that feeling right now, because it is still buried inside your heart,

EXERCISE 30–FORMAT FOR HEALING CHILDHOOD PAIN
(Cont'd)

and it's been there for a long long time...Just breathe into it...Take a moment to remember.

What happened that hurt you so much? Did someone say something mean to you? Did someone hit you? Did someone ignore you, or act cold to you? Did someone leave you? Did someone disappoint you? Did you lose something? Go back, and feel how betrayed you felt, feel how much it hurt you so deep inside...Think about how it was....

What did you want to say to that person who hurt you, what did you really want, and who did you want to ask for what you wanted...maybe you wanted to say..."Mommy, please don't tell me I'm bad...please be proud of me and love me..." or maybe you wanted to say..."Daddy, please don't go away and leave us all alone." "Please don't leave me Daddy!" Tell yourself that it is all right for you to feel all those feelings again...Remember how scared you were....

Remember what you did when you were hurt. Did you hide in your room and cry? Did you curl up under the covers where no one could find you? Did you run to a brother or sister or family member to be comforted? Did you hide the feelings inside? Did you get angry and throw a temper tantrum? Feel all those hurts now, all that pain from long ago, every time you felt unloved, unappreciated, frightened, neglected, misunderstood, lonely, angry, and feel the place inside where that hurt child still lives, hiding behind your protective walls because you don't want to feel any more pain, you don't want to be hurt anymore. Feel that hurt place inside of you....

What did you need to feel better when you felt so hurt? What did you need when you were frightened or in pain? Did you want your Daddy to come and hold you in his arms and tell you he understood your pain and he'd protect you? Did you want your Mommy to be there to kiss you and hear your pain and tell you everything would be all right? Did you want someone to promise you they wouldn't hurt you anymore? Feel how much you just wanted

EXERCISE 30–FORMAT FOR HEALING CHILDHOOD PAIN
(Cont'd)

someone to understand your pain, how much you just wanted someone to be there to hold you and make it better...and how scared you were that no one would ever make it better for you, no one would ever really understand how much you hurt...No one would ever love you the way you wanted to be loved...Remember how it felt....

And now, reach out and take my hands...This is a time to let that little child out, to let go of the pain you've been carrying around for so long, to let the pain out and let it be healed by the love I will give you...I want you to imagine that the person who hurt you is sitting in front of you...And I want you to ask that person for what you really wanted...Imagine you are talking right to that person...So you will be saying..."A time I felt hurt growing up was... What I really wanted to say was..." And I will be there to listen and love you silently. Take five to ten minutes to pour out as many incidents as you can remember. And you can begin now."

AFTER COMPLETING THIS PART OF THE EXERCISE: Sit back and close your eyes again and listen to your partner read the following:

"Take a big deep breath into your heart, feel all that pain releasing, feel all the walls tumbling down–and feel inside of you whatever your child needs to feel better...What does (he)(she) need to hear? How does (he)(she) need to be held? Ask your child what (he)(she) needs now...and this is a beautiful opportunity for you to give that child the love and comfort (he)(she) has always wanted. Feel that child inside of you, and reach out and ask me for what you want...how you want to be loved and comforted. Imagine I am all the people who hurt you, all the people you needed love from and who didn't give it to you...And just let the little child pour (his)(her) heart out and say "Please don't leave me, Please love me, I need you so much, I get so afraid...." Whatever you want to say...Just let the little child cry and talk, and I'm going to reach out and hold that

EXERCISE 30–FORMAT FOR HEALING CHILDHOOD PAIN
(Cont'd)

little child as if (he)(she) were my own, and comfort (him)(her), and love (him)(her) and say all the things (he)(she) needs to hear, and just let my love heal it, shower (him)(her) with love and make (him)(her) feel safe again. Let your child just collapse into feeling all the hurt and I will be there to give (him)(her) all the love (he)(she) ever wanted.

WHEN THE FIRST PERSON IS DONE: Thank your partner, and then switch so your partner has a chance to be healed. It's time for him/her to be the little child and to reach out for healing, and for you to be the loving comforter and help him/her to heal all the hurts inside. When you are ready you can begin.

WHEN THE SECOND PERSON IS DONE: Reach out and thank your partner for loving you so perfectly, and spend some time together sharing your healing.

EXERCISE 31–SELF-FORGIVENESS AND SELF-LOVE
To Be Used When Judging/Blaming Yourself

You can read this visualization to yourself anytime. Or better yet, have someone read it to you or make a tape for yourself that you can listen to anytime. You can use this visualization whenever you are feeling down on yourself for any reason.

Relax in your chair and close your eyes. Take some deep breaths and let them out with a sigh. Shake out any tension in your body and just relax. Relax. Allow your mind to drift back in time...and let your memories go back to a time when you were very young. Begin to see a movie of your life going backwards.... Back...back...to a time when you were very hurt. Maybe your mother or father or a grandparent yelled at you or ridiculed you, laughed at you, called you names, hit you. And you had no one to go to comfort you. And remember a time when you were upset, when you were crying, when you were alone and there was no one to comfort you. See yourself alone in your bedroom...See your shoes and the kind of clothes you wore...See yourself as you were: see how small you were, how soft you were. And feel how sad you were and how alone and how scared...And feel how overwhelming all those feelings felt in your young tender body. Just feel how all alone you were.

And now, imagine yourself as you are now quietly going into the room where your little girl or boy is...Take a moment to see yourself crying, all alone...maybe thinking that it's all your fault...or that nobody cares...or that you're going to die...and then as your grown-up self, go over to your little self and take your little self in your arms and tell (him)(her) who you are and that it's going to be all right...that you survived this pain and lived...and that you've come back to comfort (him)(her).

And now put your little self on your grown-up lap and hold (him)(her) close to you and use all of your adult resources comfort (him)(her). Feel how warm (he)(she) is, feel the softness of the skin on (his)(her) little face as you brush the tears away, feel the soft silkiness of (his)(her) hair as you stoke it and murmur soft words of

EXERCISE 31–SELF-FORGIVENESS AND SELF-LOVE (Cont'd)

love. Feel how tightly he/she holds you and how he or she gradually relaxes and stops crying as he/she starts to open to your healing love...And tell your little self that you'll never have to hurt in solitude and loneliness again, that you will take care of yourself and love yourself whenever that little child needs you in the future.

And when you feel ready, take that little child and actually pull (him)(her) inside of you...Feel (him)(her) enter your body. That little child is a part of you, a spontaneous and energetic part of your life. Take in the aliveness, the curiosity, the creativity, the sense of wonder of your little child. Feel that energy within you and know that you will be able share it with your inner child. Just sit for a moment and relax and enjoy what you're feeling. Remember how intense you were, how full of life, how interested and curious and loving...How life was full of wonder...Let those feelings spread throughout your body...And when you're ready, open your eyes and come back to the now.

You *never* need to punish yourself or hate yourself. Inflicting pain on yourself through self-judgement or self-blame is not loving behavior. Next time you hurt or are angry with yourself or are in any way judging yourself or your state of being or your (lack of) accomplishments, try *loving* yourself for what you feel, have, are and do. Remember that you had good, important reasons for developing those protections. If you can take that crucial step of loving yourself for whatever you hate about yourself, you will open the door to being able to see the erroneous beliefs that caused you to develop your protections in the first place. Your little child needed and deserved to be understood and loved...so do you.

THE WAY OF TRANSFORMATION

The man who, being really on the Way, falls upon hard times in the world will not, as a consequence, turn to that friend who offers him refuge and comfort and encourages his old self to survive. Rather, he will seek out someone who will faithfully and inexorably help him to risk himself, so that he may endure the suffering and pass courageously through it, thus making of it a "raft that leads to the far shore." Only to the extent that man exposes himself over and over again to annihilation, can that which is indestructible arise within him. In this lies the dignity of daring. Thus, the aim of practice is not to develop an attitude which allows a man to acquire a state of harmony and peace wherein nothing can ever trouble him. On the contrary, practice should teach him to let himself be assaulted, perturbed, moved, insulted, broken and battered—that is to say, it should enable him to dare to let go his futile hankering after harmony, surcease from pain, and a comfortable life in order that he may discover, in doing battle with the forces that oppose him, that which awaits him beyond the world of opposites. The first necessity is that we should have the courage to face life, and to encounter all that is most perilous in the world. Only if we venture repeatedly through zones of annihilation can our contact with Divine Being, which is beyond annihilation, become firm and stable. The more a man learns whole-heartedly to confront the world that threatens him with isolation, the more are the depths of the Ground of Being revealed and the possibilities of new life and Becoming opened.

*From the book, **The Way of Transformation**
by Karlfried Gräf von Durckheim*

CHAPTER

·9·

CONTINUING THE PROCESS

Becoming a more loving human being is a lifelong process. It is an ideal that you can always move closer to. It doesn't matter how much you are motivated to work at it, where you start, or where you end. The only thing that's important is that you're in the process.

You can look forward to your life and relationships improving as you become more loving. There probably won't be any drastic, sudden changes, although that is possible. Changes usually occur slowly, with plenty of ups and downs. Your ego will fight the changes tooth and nail, and your ego is very powerful. Your conscious Will will have to be dedicated to this process if you are to be very successful at it.

Dedication means using the formats for exploration in Chapter 4 over and over again. It means continuing to make your personal growth and learning a high priority. It means remembering that *everything* in your life is an opportunity to learn and be grateful (which is the subject of Exercise 35). Tuning into what others have found in their journeys can also be a big help in your learning process, so we've included a recommended reading list.

Connecting with like-minded people is very important. Any group that fosters personal responsibility and spirituality would most likely be supportive. You could form your own support group of people trying to put the principles of loving behavior into practice. A support group could be just you and one other person, or more people who want to learn. Exercise 36 contains a few suggestions as to how to get one started.

Doing the exercises in this book with a close friend or significant other can deepen them. Discuss the concepts. Many of the ideas presented fly in the face of traditional wisdom. Ideas about responsibility, right and wrong, men, women, children and human beings are deeply ingrained. But many of them are erroneous. This is a spiritual, psychological and emotional journey. And the only person who has all the answers for you is YOU. Inside of you lies the truth. Avoid those who only want to indoctrinate you into their truth. Surround yourself with people whose intent is to help you find your truth while they're finding theirs.

The three exercises that follow will be helpful in your on-going and deepening understanding of this material when you're working with other people.

EXERCISE 32–BEING A HELPER

The following ideas are offered to help you understand more about your role when you are helping another person explore and learn about himself/herself.

Objectives: To help another person:

1.   Understand and learn from her feelings and behavior.

2.   Become aware *when* her intent is to protect (to not want to understand and learn from feelings) and *how* she is protecting. (See list of what to look for on next page.)

3.   Explore the beliefs and fears behind her protections and assume personal responsibility for her own learning.

4.   Use the Formats for Learning provided in this workbook.

What this looks like:

> To "get with" people who are exploring their feelings means to be with them totally, not thinking about your own thoughts on the subject, not thinking about what you will say next. It's not a conversation. It means to be interested and caring enough to feel into them deeply and to offer them loving support when they get in touch with their pain and tears. It is your opportunity to be curious. Your job is to help them tune in to the beliefs they're trying to find.
>
> Your comments and questions are those that help another person to stay focused and go deeper into her feelings, to help him/her differentiate between thinking and feeling. When awarenesses come out of a feeling experience, they are usually more meaningful.
>
> Point out the body language that's saying something, i.e., "You seem real tight. Your body looks all tied up. Your eyes seem sad. You look scared. What are you feel right now?" *Always* check out nonverbal messages.
>
> For the most part, you will focus on the protections rather than the story.
>
> Stay in the moment.

EXERCISE 32-BEING A HELPER (Cont'd)

Tune into your own feeling reactions. Are you feeling the explorer's feelings, or is it an intellectual exercise?

Examples of helpful questions are:

What are you feeling right now?
What are you wanting right now?
What are you wanting to learn about right now?
What do you think your intent is right now?
What do you think are the important reasons you have for feeling this way?
What are you unhappy about?
Why does that make you feel unhappy?
What are you doing that keeps you from getting what you want?

Listen and focus on beliefs, i.e.:

What is the belief behind your feeling?
Where did you get that belief?
Why do you believe that?
Is it accurate?

When you find it difficult to give genuine caring and interest and help another person assume personal responsibility for her own learning, you have an opportunity to engage in your own important learning. To facilitate another, you need to put aside your own fears and beliefs. When you find the issue at hand is tapping into your fears and protections, you may need to stop and explore your protections, and your partner's reaction to your protections. Exploring the beliefs behind your protections is what makes you a more helpful facilitator.

EXERCISE 33–OBSERVING AS A THIRD PARTY

Another interesting exercise is to have three people work together in the exploration process. While a helper is working with an explorer, the third person can act as an observer. The observer is there to help the helper stay on track. It's so easy to slip out of being a helper and into being a caretaker that this exercise can be very valuable.

Objectives:

> To observe an interaction between a helper and an explorer and to work with the helper to keep the exploration on a learning track.

> To help the helper become aware of when her intent changes to protecting instead of helping and to help her become aware of how she is protecting.

> To help the helper become aware of when the explorer's intent changes to protecting instead of learning and to help the helper become aware of how the explorer is protecting.

What to look for:

> Explanations
> Accusations, blaming
> Rationalizations
> Excuses
> Attacking
> Defending
> Criticizing
> Analyzing
> Problem solving
> Making others responsible, wrong
> Being a helpless victim, not taking responsibility
> Not wanting to learn about self
> Anything other than an interest in learning

EXERCISE 33–OBSERVING AS A THIRD PARTY (Cont'd)

Learn to tune in to your feelings. When you feel uncomfortable, anxious, defensive, chances are the interaction you are observing has left the learning track. Your own inner tension alerts you to another's protections as well as you own.

Your task is not to judge, analyze, problem solve, therapize–merely to gently *point out* your observations or ask questions only to the helper.

Helpful interventions might be:

Are you feeling attacked right now? I'm feeling uncomfortable right now. I've got a weight in the pit of my stomach, which I usually get when I feel blamed. What are you feeling?

You seem to be "leading the witness." Are you having difficulty staying with her?

The interaction seems to have deteriorated into a lot of defensiveness. How are you feeling about it?

You seem to be giving the explorer advice. Is it hard for you to learn right? Why would you rather problem-solve?

EXERCISE 34–TWO COUPLES HELPING EACH OTHER

A fascinating learning experience for couples is for two couples to work together in an exploration process.

1. In this exercise each person will partner with the person of the opposite sex in the other couple.

2. One set of partners will explore together taking turns being an explorer and a helper.

3. Each person chooses something he/she would like to learn about. Then take five minutes to be an explorer,and then 5 minutes to be a helper. The other set of partners will be silent observers.

4. In addition to whatever learning takes place during the exploration, you will have a wonderful opportunity for each person to become aware of how different they are with another person. The participating couple may find themselves having a much easier time being both the explorer and the helper than they each have with their own partners. The observers may see their mates in an entirely different light. Reactions like "I never believed he could be so open" are not uncommon.

5. Noting the differences can then lead into discussions about why those differences are there. How come we are different with others? What is it in our interactions that produces the deadness, the defensiveness, etc? Each person can have the opportunity to learn about his and her part of the system.

EXERCISE 35–APPRECIATING YOUR LIFE

The purpose of this exercise is to practice learning to appreciate *everything* in your life as a gift, as an opportunity being presented to for your higher good. Appreciating both positive and negative experiences is a goal toward learning to be at peace with whatever is in your life. A saying we've always liked is, "Life gives you two kinds of experiences–positive and negative. For those who learn from their negative experiences, life offers only one kind of experience."

Most people can appreciate positive things, even though we sometimes fail to acknowledge our appreciation. But appreciating the opportunities given by the difficulties in our lives is a very different story. We are most likely to say or think, "No! I don't *want* this!" "I don't deserve this," "I don't want to feel this way," or "Why me?" (said as a victim).

PART 1–Appreciating the "Positive" Experiences

Begin by appreciating those people who have helped you learn and affirm yourself. Think about the people in your life who have helped you or supported you when you were in need or in difficult times–the people who had faith in you. Among these special people may be grandparents, parents, teachers, friends or friends' parents.

1. Write your thoughts about the positive influence each one has had on your life.

2. Whenever possible, tell that person your feelings in person, on the phone, or by sending a letter or card.

3. If you have difficulty finding, feeling, and/or expressing your positive feelings, discover the self-limiting beliefs that are blocking you.

EXERCISE 35–APPRECIATING YOUR LIFE (Cont'd)

PART 2–Appreciating "Negative" Experiences

There are those people or situations in your life currently which are difficult for you–a specific child, an illness, your mate, a parent, a sibling, and ex-mate or lover, an employee, boss, client, student. Any past situation that you feel upset about or victimized by is still unresolved and, therefore, still exists in the present.

This exercise is not just making lemonade out of lemons or looking for the silver lining, it is an opportunity to look deeply within and discover how and/or why you are not being loving to yourself or to another person. For example, any illness gives you the opportunity to look at your beliefs about things like: how illness is contracted and cured, your feelings about being sick and needy, death (if it's a serious illness), your life style that may have contributed to your body's defense system being depleted, or any emotionally stuck places. Illness is not just about getting better, it's about learning to create better health.

The same thing is true for people in your life. People often complain that while one of their children is a delight, "We got one that drives us nuts." That one is your teacher. Learning to love that child will be your best and most expanding lesson.

If you are married to a man/woman who is so intelligent and powerful that you find yourself getting defensive or giving in, that is your opportunity to confront your insecurities and the beliefs that are causing them.

If you feel threatened or intimidated by anyone in your life, that person is there to give you the opportunity to learn how to create peace instead of anxiety. With each person or situation, accept that he/she/it is a gift in your life to teach you something very important for your emotional and spiritual development. Ask yourself the following questions:

1. Why am I reacting so intensely? What is the button being pushed? Who is this person reminding me of?

EXERCISE 35–APPRECIATING YOUR LIFE (Cont'd)

    2. What is my lesson here?

    3. What are the self-limiting beliefs that I need to resolve?

PART 3–Appreciating Everyday Problems

It's not a large step, but a very significant one to go from appreciating and accepting the major problems in your life to appreciating and learning from even the minor irritations: disappointments; unmet expectations; things not going your way, things not on schedule; the computer crashing and wiping out two hours of work; your wife or husband being late, again; the freeway being jammed; your secretary forgetting to make an important change in your appointment schedule; your business partner not holding up his end of a commitment; your child being disrespectful.

    1. What is my spiritual lesson? What does this conflict have to teach me about letting go and having faith?

    2. How can I turn this irritation into a positive experience, one that will allow me to feel peaceful and increase my self-esteem?

    3. What self-limiting beliefs are getting in the way of that?

EXERCISE 36–JOIN A SUPPORT GROUP

One of the most exciting and valuable on-going experiences occurs when like-minded people connect. Meeting together to share your process can be helpful in many ways.

The major value of a support group is as a resource when you get stuck, and you will get stuck. The ideas you are working with from this book are so different from your previous programming that doubts, questions, and difficulties will arise. Most people are not good at getting through their stuck places and eventually give up. A support group can be a place where you get additional input that may free your thinking.

In a support group, you will also share your "highs". Hearing the successes of others is an important motivation to know that there is a rainbow in this storm. In hearing the successes of others, you may get some additional ideas as to where you might be stuck. You may also judge yourself for not being "further ahead." If that happens, you have another wonderful opportunity to learn about the self-limiting beliefs by which you judge yourself.

The purpose of the group is not to therapize or tell people what to do, but to find answers to stuck places and practice the intention to learn. The focus will be on finding the loving (caring) behavior in a conflict and discovering the fears and beliefs that are blocking that behavior.

Structure of the Meetings

PART 1 – 20 minutes – Sharing

> This is a time for group members to share their excitement and frustrations, the positive things that are happening as a result of becoming more loving and any stuck places they might be experiencing.

PART 2 – 20 minutes – Discuss reading

EXERCISE 36–JOIN A SUPPORT GROUP (Cont'd)

Each week, read aloud from *From Conflict to Caring* and discuss the material. The following are typical assignments: Meeting 1, pages 14-18; Meeting 2, pages 18-22; Meeting 3, pages 22-26; etc.

PART 3 – 10 minutes – Meditation

Do a centering exercise. This might be just a ten minute deep breathing meditation or listening to any centering tape which a member has found helpful.

PART 4 – 50 minutes – Finding the loving behavior

A. 20 minutes–Complete the following format:

1. What was the conflict?

2. Describe your reaction.

3. If your reaction did not leave you feeling peaceful and enhance your self-esteem, you know it was not a loving response. What were the results of your behavior:

   a. Between you and the other person?

   b. To yourself?

4. What would a loving response be? What response would promote personal responsi-bility and enhance your self-esteem?

5. What fears and beliefs would stop you from this behavior?

B. 10 minutes–Find a partner and take five minutes each to help each other with questions 4 and 5.

EXERCISE 36–JOIN A SUPPORT GROUP (Cont'd)

C.   20 minutes–Get back together as a group and help anyone who requests help in deepening their understanding of questions 4 and 5.

PART 5 – 20 minutes – Social time!

Enjoy each other and use whatever conflicts arise interpersonally as wonderful opportunities to use the Formats for Learning.

We have found that leaderless groups don't work very well unless they are structured, so we strongly recommend that you follow the structure as closely as possible.

A support group is not a therapy group. It is, however, a way for people who share the same values of loving behavior and the intent to learn to come together as they explore themselves and each other.

Setting Up a Group

The group should consist of between 6 and 10 members. Meetings can be held at someone's home, and the responsibility of refreshments (if the group decides to have them) can be shared or rotated. Meeting from 7:30 to 9:30 p.m. every two weeks on a week-night seems to work out well, although each group will eventually evolve its own best schedule. Discuss schedules well in advance, planning for vacations, trips and holidays. When it occasionally becomes difficult to make the extra effort to get to a meeting, it is comforting to know that others are also making that same effort.

One member should assume the role of leader. The leadership can be changed periodically to give other members the opportunity for leadership experience. The leader takes the responsibility to schedule and organize the meetings. Initially he/she will make up a group roster and have copies available at the first

EXERCISE 36–JOIN A SUPPORT GROUP (Cont'd)

meeting. Any cost incurred by the leader should be shared by the group.

Generally, the role of the leader is to see that the schedule for the meeting is kept. It is important to remember that *this is not group therapy!* Each group member should be encouraged to take responsibility for his or her own learning and to inform the group of his/her needs or feelings about the group. *The leader should be prepared to communicate any serious conflicts, unresolved issues, or philosophical questions to the Intention Training office, and not allow them to side-track meetings.*

How To Find People

An interesting dilemma is how to find like-minded people. The first thing it takes is your intention to connect with those people. Once you get that clearly set in your mind, then turn your attention to how you might connect with people who are familiar with our books. The following suggestions are only a few of the many possibilities:

1. Check with your local bookstores; they may be able to help you contact people who have expressed interest in our work.

2. Put up notices in places that might attract people interesting in learning about themselves, e.g., churches, healing centers, libraries.

3. Call the Intention Training Office and ask us if we know of people in your area. We might be able to link you up with a few people, and if we can't, we'll at least put you on our database as interested.

As you find other ways that work for you, we'd really appreciate your sharing them with us.

EXERCISE 37–THE LEARNING LOG

The learning log can be xeroxed and used to keep track of and focus on your learning.

ISSUE EXPLORED: DATE:

PROTECTIONS EXPLORED:

1.   New understandings I gained about my beliefs concerning:

        The issue

        My protections

2.   What have I learned about how to get out of my protected position?

3.   How do I feel about myself right now and what has led to these feelings?

4.   What do I need to learn more about?

RECOMMENDED READING

Your Child's Self Esteem	Dorothy Briggs
To Love Is To Be Happy With	Barry Neil Kaufman
Giant Steps	Barry Neil Kaufman
Hearts That We Broke Long Ago	Merle Shain
Making Peace With Your Parents	Harold Bloomfield
For Your Own Good	Alice Miller
Teach Only Love	Gerald Jampolsky
Love Is Letting Go Of Fear	Gerald Jampolsky
Bridge Across Forever	Richard Bach
The Road Less Traveled	M. Scott Peck
Daughters Of Copper Woman	Ann Cameron
Your Erroneous Zones	Wayne Dyer
The Course in Miracles	The Foundation for Inner Peace
Women Who Love Too Much	Robin Norwood
Breaking Free From Compulsive Eating	Geneen Roth
The Search for Existential Identity	J.F.T. Bugental
Men Who Hate Women and The Women Who Love Them	Susan Forward
When Society Becomes an Addict	Anne Wilson Schaef
The Magic of Conflict	Tom Crum
Women and Self-Esteem	Linda Tschirhart Sanford and Mary Ellen Donovan
The Chalice and the Blade	Riane Eisler
How Can I Help?	Ram Dass & Paul Gorman
Love, Medicine and Miracles	Bernie Siegel

AVAILABLE FROM INTENTION TRAINING

Books by Jordan and Margaret Paul

	Retail	From IT
Do I Have to Give Up Me to Be Loved By You?	10.95	10.95
If You Really Loved Me...	10.95	10.95
From Conflict to Caring	16.95	11.95
Free to Love	5.95	3.95

Audio Cassettes from Jordan and Margaret Paul

From Conflict to Intimacy and Beyond	44.95	34.95

(Based on *Do I Have to Give Up Me to Be Loved by You?*
Six cassettes - three hours; lecture plus questions and answers)

Exploring IF YOU REALLY LOVED ME	36.95	29.95

(Four cassettes -
Two hours and twenty minutes.; lecture plus questions and answers)

From Fear & Control to Love and Freedom	8.95	8.95

(With Dr. Susan Forward)

You Are Your Higher Self	8.95	5.95

(Visualization Tape)

- - - - - - - - - - - - - - - - -

	How Many	Unit Price	Total
Do I Have to Give Up Me to Be Loved By You?	_____	10.95	_____
If You Really Loved Me...	_____	10.95	_____
From Conflict to Caring	_____	11.95	_____
Free to Love	_____	3.95	_____
From Conflict to Intimacy and Beyond	_____	34.95	_____
Exploring If You Really Loved Me	_____	29.95	_____
From Fear & Control to Love and Freedom	_____	8.95	_____
You Are Your Higher Self	_____	5.95	_____

Shipping and handling.   3.00

Subtotal _____

With orders of more than $50, deduct an additional 10%.
California residents add 6.5% sales tax. _____

TOTAL _____

INTENTION TRAINING
2531 Sawtelle Blvd. #42 • Los Angeles, CA 90064
(213) 390-5993

Comments about Jordan and Margaret Paul's other books:

Do I Have to Give Up Me to Be Loved by You?

"The most important, useful and powerful book I have read on couple therapy since Virginia Satir's *Conjoint Family Therapy...* One of the rare books that is both useful to the lay audience and indispensable for the clinician."

> DENNIS JAFFE, Ph.D., author of *Healing from Within*

"Excellent! Fresh useful insights, great diagrams, terrific dialogue, upbeat...It's got it all!"

> HAROLD H. BLOOMFIELD, M.D., author of *Making Peace with Your Parents*

If You Really Loved Me...

"A course in parenting designed to produce miracles. I endorse this marvelous book enthusiastically."

> Wayne Dyer, Ph.D., author of *Your Erroneous Zones*

"This is a breakthrough book. The Pauls teach a new technique for dealing with human relationships that really works. This approach that leads to becoming truly loving toward our children and ourselves, enhancing self-esteem, growth, and personal power."

> Walter Brackelmanns, M.D., Child Psychiatrist
> Assoc. Professor of Clinical Psychiatry, U.C.L.A

"The Pauls' ideas, although eternal in principle, have never been made so practical and applicable. This is a fresh, new approach to being a parent. Seeing how conflict can be a way for parents and children to learn and grow is wonderful, and opens up marvelous possibilities to have fun in the process. You have shown us all how to truly experience love for ourselves as well as for our children."

> Rev. Peggy Bassett,
> Huntington Beach Church of Religious Science

"This book fulfills a tremendous need. It takes extremely complicated and subtle ideas and enables us to understand and act on them. It looks at parents' responsibility without affixing guilt. It's like seeing a video of how conflict works in your very own family. I will recommend this book to every family I'm working with and every therapist I train."

> JILLA WOLSEY, Past President, California Association of Marriage and Family Therapists

PRINCIPLES FOR RELATIONSHIPS

1. *My relationships are my opportunity to express myself as a loving person. How I express my love is a function of my own willingness to do so, not the result of how another person behaves.*

2. *Any difficult or painful moment in my relationships is a new opportunity for me to develop as a loving person. At the moment of conflict, I can choose to blame the other and the relationship, or, by my willingness to learn from the experience, use the occasion to expand more fully my ability to love and learn.*

3. *I am the one who generates my experience of my relationships through how I choose to act and react to whatever anyone does, and I am solely responsible for my feelings.*

4. *All my life's partners (mate, children, parents, friends, business associates) love me in their Higher Selves as I love them in my Higher Self. My life partners are lovable in their Higher Selves as I am lovable in my Higher Self.*

5. *I can experience love and satisfaction whenever I choose. These feelings are possible at any time and place and in any circumstance, whenever I choose to be who I really am, my Higher Self.*